D0210814

DATE DUE

COLLECTIONS
FOR YOUNG SCHOLARS™
VOLUME 4 BOOK 2

Surviving

Technology

Colonial Life

Art by Leah Palmer Preiss

COLLECTIONS FOR YOUNG SCHOLARS™

VOLUME 4 BOOK 2

PROGRAM AUTHORS
Carl Bereiter
Ann Brown
Marlene Scardamalia
Valerie Anderson
Joe Campione

CONSULTING AUTHORS
Michael Pressley
Iva Carruthers
Bill Pinkney

OPEN COURT PUBLISHING COMPANY
CHICAGO AND PERU, ILLINOIS

CHAIRMAN
M. Blouke Carus

PRESIDENT
André W. Carus

EDUCATION DIRECTOR
Carl Bereiter

CONCEPT
Barbara Conteh

EXECUTIVE EDITOR
Shirley Graudin

MANAGING EDITOR
Sheelagh McGurn

PROJECT EDITOR
Wiley Blevins

ART DIRECTOR
John Grandits

VICE-PRESIDENT, PRODUCTION
AND MANUFACTURING
Chris Vancalbergh

PERMISSIONS COORDINATOR
Diane Sikora

COVER ARTIST
Leah Palmer Preiss

ACKNOWLEDGMENTS

Grateful acknowledgment is given to the following publishers and copyright owners for permission granted to reprint selections from their publications. All possible care has been taken to trace ownership and secure permission for each selection included.

Atheneum Publishers, an imprint of Macmillan Publishing Co.: An excerpt entitled "Nachito's Teachings" from *Medicine Walk* by Ardath Mayhar, copyright © 1985 by Ardath Mayhar. "Walk Together Children" from *Walk Together Children: Black American Spirituals* selected and illustrated by Ashley Bryan, copyright © 1974 by Ashley Bryan. "Many Thousand Gone" from *I'm Going to Sing: Black American Spirituals* selected and illustrated by Ashley Bryan, copyright © 1982 by Ashley Bryan.

Carolrhoda Books, Inc., Minneapolis, MN: An excerpt from *Arctic Explorer: The Story of Matthew Henson* by Jeri Ferris, text copyright © 1989 by Jeri Ferris.

Childrens Press, Inc., Chicago: "Jamestown: First Permanent English Settlement in America" and "Pocahontas" from *The Virginia Colony* by Dennis B. Fradin, copyright © 1986 by Childrens Press, Inc. An excerpt from *The Massachusetts Colony* by Dennis B. Fradin, copyright © 1986 by Childrens Press, Inc. "Phillis Wheatley: Poet" from *Extraordinary Black Americans from Colonial to Contemporary Times* by Susan Altman, copyright © 1989 by Childrens Press, Inc. "Life in Philadelphia" from *The Pennsylvania Colony* by Dennis B. Fradin, copyright © 1988 by Childrens Press, Inc.

Cobblestone Publishing, Inc.: "First Conflicts and Sharp Beginnings" by Duane Damon and "The Voyage of the Mayflower" by Patricia M. Whalen from the November 1989 issue of *Cobblestone* magazine: *Pilgrims to a New World*, copyright © 1989 by Cobblestone Publishing, Inc. "Judith: The Life of a Slave" by Cathleene Hellier and Brandon Miller from the February 1990 issue of *Cobblestone* magazine: *The People of Williamsburg*, copyright © 1990 by Cobblestone Publishing, Inc., 7 School Street, Peterborough, NH 03458.

Doubleday, a division of Bantam Doubleday Dell Publishing Group, Inc., and Vallentine Mitchell & Co. Ltd.: An excerpt from *Anne Frank: The Diary of a Young Girl* by Anne Frank, translated from the Dutch by B. M. Mooyaart-Doubleday, copyright 1952 by Otto H. Frank.

Dutton Children's Books, a division of Penguin Books USA Inc.: "Solitude" from *Now We Are Six* by A. A. Milne, copyright 1927 by E. P. Dutton, copyright © renewed 1955 by A. A. Milne.

Ganado Mission to the Navajo Indians, Ganado, AZ: "Progress" from *Songs of Marcelino* by Edith Agnew, copyright 1935, 1940, 1953 by Edith Agnew.

David R. Godine, Publishers, Inc., Boston: An excerpt from *Thrashin' Time: Harvest Days in the Dakotas* by David Weitzman, copyright © 1991 by David Weitzman.

Greenwillow Books, a division of William Morrow & Co., Inc., and Walter H. Lorraine: *McBroom and the Big Wind* by Sid Fleischman, illustrated by Walter H. Lorraine, text copyright © 1967 by Sid Fleischman, illustrations copyright © 1982 by Walter H. Lorraine.

HarperCollins Publishers: An excerpt from *The Big Wave* by Pearl S. Buck, copyright 1947 by The Curtis Publishing Co., copyright 1948, © 1976 by Pearl S. Buck. An excerpt from "The Wonderful Machine" from *Little House in the Big Woods* by Laura Ingalls Wilder, illustrated by Garth Williams, text copyright 1932 by Laura Ingalls Wilder, copyright © renewed 1960 by Roger L. MacBride, illustrations copyright 1953 by Garth Williams, copyright © renewed 1981 by Garth Williams. An excerpt from *The Fighting Ground* by Avi, copyright © 1984 by Avi Wortis.

Houghton Mifflin Co.: An excerpt from *Island of the Blue Dolphins* by Scott O'Dell, copyright © 1960, copyright © renewed 1988 by Scott O'Dell.

Alfred A. Knopf, Inc.: "Freedom" from *The Panther and the Lash* by Langston Hughes, copyright © 1967 by Arna Bontemps and George Houston Bass.

Little, Brown and Co.: "The Grasshopper" from *One at a Time* by David McCord, copyright 1952 by David McCord.

Lothrop, Lee & Shepard, a division of William Morrow & Co., Inc.: "The Messenger" and an excerpt from "The Workhorse" from *Once Upon a Horse* by Suzanne Jurmain, copyright © 1989 by Suzanne Jurmain.

continued on page 320

SURVIVING
ℑ

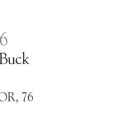

TECHNOLOGY

COLONIAL LIFE

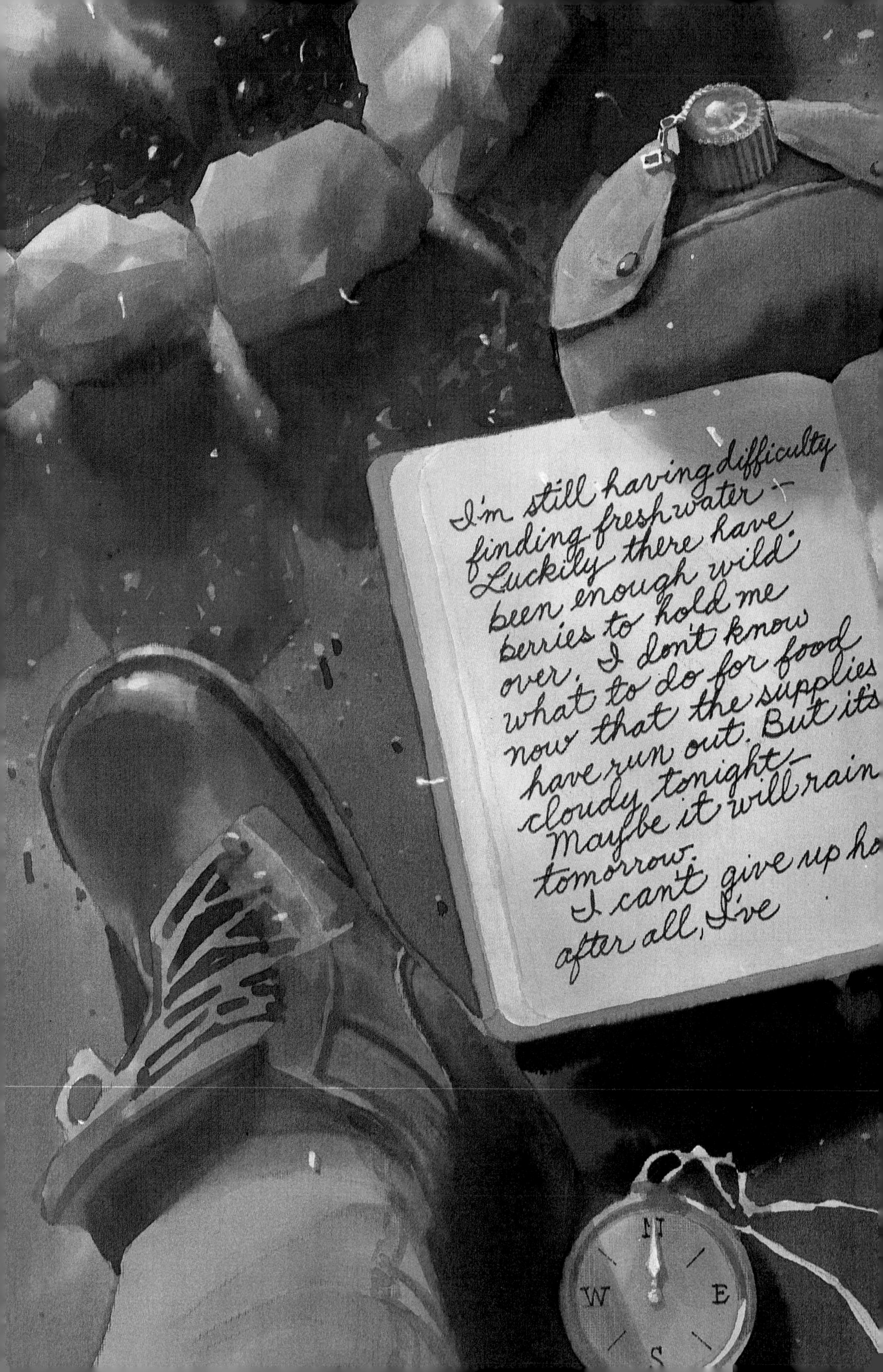
I'm still having difficulty
finding fresh water.
Luckily there have
been enough wild
berries to hold me
over. I don't know
what to do for food
now that the supplies
have run out. But it's
cloudy tonight—
Maybe it will rain
tomorrow.
I can't give up ho
after all, I've
N
W
E

SURVIVING

13

ARCTIC EXPLORER:
THE STORY OF
MATTHEW HENSON
Jeri Ferris

Library of Congress/PHOTRI

Matthew Henson was the first African-American
explorer to reach the North Pole. Before he made this
famous expedition, he went on several trips to the arctic region
with Robert Peary. During these trips, Henson learned the
skills that would make him a great explorer. In this excerpt
about Henson's first arctic journey, Peary has planned an
expedition to North Greenland. He has little money and has
asked Henson to help him without pay. Henson is eager to go.
His job is to learn the survival techniques used by the Eskimos
as they face the harsh, cold climate.

"It was in June 1891," Matt Henson wrote, "that I started on my first trip to the Arctic regions, as a member of what was known as the 'North Greenland Expedition.'"

America's newspapers predicted disaster. A small group of inexperienced men trying to survive in a frozen place that had killed better men than they? Impossible. Then reporters learned that a woman was going too—the new Mrs. Peary. "Now we know he's crazy!" said one newspaper about Peary.

Josephine Peary listed the expedition members in her diary: "Dr. Cook, Mr. Gibson, Mr. Astrup, Mr. Verhoeff, and Mr. Peary's faithful attendant in his surveying labors in Nicaragua, Matt Henson." The ship, *Kite*, was so small that the people and supplies barely fit. They were going to be gone for a year and a half, so they needed a lot of supplies. There were crates of food (enough for two and a half years, just to be safe) and cans of pemmican, the beef-fat-raisin

Members of the 1891–1892 North Greenland Expedition (left to right):
Cook, Henson, Astrup, Verhoeff, and Gibson. Josephine and Robert Peary
are standing in back. John Verhoeff fell into a crevasse in Greenland in the
spring of 1892 while exploring and was never seen again.

mixture that the men and dogs would eat while crossing the
ice cap. There were skis and snowshoes, guns and ammunition, sledges, woolen clothing, a stove, pots and pans, and
camera equipment. And after the last one hundred tons of
coal was piled on deck, Matt could hardly find a place to set
down his hammer and nails while he put together the wood
frame for their base camp house.

The *Kite* plunged on through the Atlantic, rolling and pitching and sending all the passengers except Henson and Peary to bed seasick. On June 21 Matt saw Greenland for the first time. Its steep, wild cliffs rose straight up from the icy water. As the *Kite* steamed north through Baffin Bay, Matt saw hundreds of icebergs—gleaming blue and white chunks of ice—from the size of small sailboats to that of enormous floating mountains. In the valleys of Greenland, Matt saw glaciers that looked like thick flowing cream, frozen into white walls. And on the very top of Greenland lay the five hundred thousand square miles of silent ice cap. Matt couldn't see it yet, but he knew it was there, waiting.

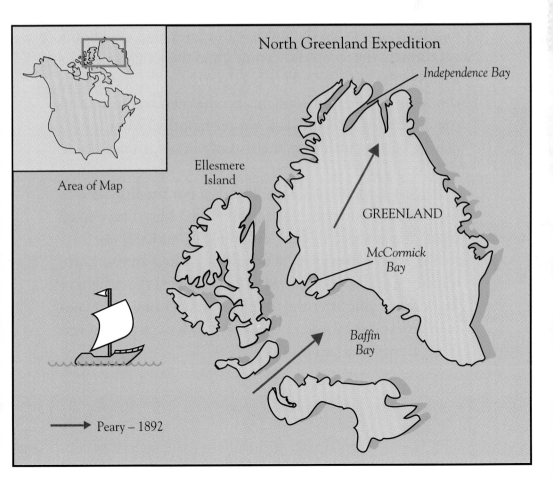

North Greenland Expedition

Independence Bay

Area of Map

Ellesmere
Island

GREENLAND

McCormick
Bay

Baffin
Bay

→ Peary – 1892

The *Kite* pushed farther north into heavy ice, which floated on the water like a field of white. There were splits and cracks in the ice, and through these cracks (called leads) the *Kite* forced its way. Sometimes there were no leads at all, and the captain would shout for more steam power. The *Kite* would dash forward and smash against the ice. Sometimes the ice would break, and the ship could continue. Sometimes it would not, and the ship would have to back up and try another way.

When the *Kite* was as far north as it could go, it dropped anchor in McCormick Bay, Greenland, and the crew unloaded the supplies. At the end of July, the *Kite* sailed for home, leaving Matthew Henson, the Pearys, and the other four men to survive the arctic winter. (A ship could only get through the ice in the summer, and the long, dangerous trip over the ice cap could only be started in the spring with the return of 24-hour sunlight. So the men had to wait in the Arctic through the dark winter months.) Matt immediately began putting up their sturdy house, to make sure they would survive.

August 8 was Matt's 25th birthday. For the first time in his life, he had a birthday celebration. Mrs. Peary fixed mock turtle soup, stew of little auk (a bird the size of a robin) with green peas, eider duck, baked beans, corn, tomatoes, and apricot pie. Matt remembered the delight of that dinner long after the tin plates were put away. Seventeen years later he said of that day, "To have a party given in my honor touched me deeply."

While Matt finished the small wooden house, the other men went to find Eskimos to join their group. (The men would have to use sign language because none of them spoke Eskimo.) Peary needed Eskimo men to help hunt polar bears and seals and walruses and reindeer and caribou and foxes for furs and meat. He needed Eskimo women to chew the furs and sew them into pants and coats. The thickest wool coat from home would be useless in the Arctic; they had to have clothing made of the same fur that kept the arctic animals warm. In exchange for their work, Peary would give the Eskimos pots and pans, needles, tools, and other useful items.

On August 18 the men returned, and with them were four Eskimos: Ikwa, his wife, and their two children. The Eskimos walked slowly up to Matt and the Pearys. Then Ikwa stepped closer to Matt and looked at him carefully. His brown face lit up with excitement as he spoke rapidly to Matt in Eskimo. Matt shook his head and tried to explain that he didn't understand, but Ikwa kept talking. Finally Ikwa took Matt's arm, pointed at the black man's skin, and said, "Inuit, Inuit!" Then Matt understood. "Inuit" must be what the Eskimos called themselves. Ikwa thought Matt was another Eskimo because he had brown skin, just as the Eskimos did. Matt looked down at the short fur-covered man, who smelled like seals and whale blubber. He looked into Ikwa's shining black eyes and smiled. From that moment on, the Eskimos called Matt "Miy Paluk," which meant "dear little Matthew," and they loved him as a brother.

Matt and an Eskimo friend return from a hunting expedition.

In September Matt, Ikwa, Dr. Cook, and the Pearys took the whale boat and went to find more Eskimos. They didn't find a single Eskimo, but they did find some unfriendly walruses.

It began when the boat got mixed up with some walruses (250 walruses, Mrs. Peary said) that were peacefully fishing for clams. One after another the startled walruses poked their heads out of the water, spitting out clam shells and flashing their white tusks. Then an angry bull walrus roared, "Ook, ook, ook!" and headed straight for the boat. The water foamed and boiled as the rest of the herd charged right behind him, speeding along like torpedoes, all roaring their battle cry and tossing their enormous gray wrinkled heads. Matt and the others knew that just one tusk through the bottom of the boat would be the end of them. Ikwa shouted and pounded on the boat to frighten the walruses away, but the walruses weren't frightened. In fact, they were so angry that they tossed the boat up and down furiously. Bracing their feet, Matt and the others fired their guns while Mrs. Peary sat in the bottom of the boat and reloaded the guns as fast as she could. At last the walruses gave up. They dove to the bottom and disappeared, leaving a shaky group of explorers in a still-rocking boat.

By the end of September, the dull red sun dipped lower each day and finally did not appear at all over the southern horizon. Every day was like a glorious sunset, with a golden, crimson glow on the mountain peaks. Then there was no sunset anymore, just one long night.

By the time the sun was gone, not to return until February, several Eskimo families were living at the camp in stone igloos (snow igloos were only used when the Eskimos traveled, following the animals whose meat and skins they needed).

That winter the men hunted by the full moon—by moonlight so bright that the blue-white ice sparkled. Peary planned for the spring trek. Astrup taught the men to ski. Gibson studied bird and animal life. Verhoeff studied rocks. Dr. Cook *wanted* to study the Eskimos by taking their pictures and measuring their bodies, but the Eskimos refused to let him near them. Finally Matt realized that they were afraid Dr. Cook would go home and make new people from the Eskimo pattern. So Matt got Ikwa to understand, and Dr. Cook got his pictures.

Meanwhile Matt studied with his Eskimo teachers. They taught him easy things, such as never to stand with his feet apart or his elbows sticking out, as this let the cold air close to his body. They taught him hard things, such as how to speak Eskimo. Matt learned, for example, that there is no Eskimo word for "hole." Instead there is a different word for "hole in igloo" or "hole in bear skin" or anything that has a hole.

Matt learned why the Eskimos smelled like walruses and seals and blubber—they *ate* walruses and seals and blubber. They also ate reindeer and polar bears and little auks. They ate the meat while it was still warm and raw and bloody; they ate it when it was frozen solid, by chipping off bite-size chunks; and sometimes they boiled it. They never ate carrots or beans or potatoes or apples or chocolate. In the Arctic the only food came from the bodies of the animals that lived there.

Matt learned how the Eskimos made the skin of a polar bear into clothing. Once the Eskimo man had killed the bear and removed its skin and scraped it as clean as he could, it was up to the Eskimo woman to finish. She had to chew the skin until all the fat was gone and it was completely soft. All day long the woman would fold the skin (with the fur folded inside), chew back and forth along the fold, make a new fold, and continue. It took two days to chew one skin. Then the woman would rest her jaws for one day before beginning on another skin. After the skin had dried, she would cut it up and sew it into a coat or

An Eskimo woman makes clothing out of an animal skin. Old Eskimo women had very short, flat teeth from chewing skins to soften them.

pants. Her needle was made of bone, her thread was made from animal sinew, and her stitches had to be very, very tiny so not a whisper of wind could get through.

For Matt's winter outfit the women made stockings of arctic hare fur, tall boots of sealskin, polar bear fur pants, a shirt made of 150 auk skins (with the feathers next to Matt's skin), a reindeer fur jacket, and a white fox fur hood that went around his face. His mittens were made of bearskin with the fur inside.

But the piercing, freezing cold, colder than the inside of a freezer, took Matt's breath away, and the howling arctic wind drove needles of snow and ice into his face. Even his new sealskin boots felt terrible, until he learned to stand still after he put them on in the morning. Then they would freeze instantly to the shape of his feet and wouldn't hurt as much.

Once Matt had his fur clothes, cold or not, he was ready to learn how to drive a sledge pulled by the 80- to 120-pound Eskimo dogs. But first, if a dog got loose, Matt had to catch him. He would drop a piece of frozen meat on the snow and dive on top of the dog as the animal snatched the meat. Then he would "grab the nearest thing grabbable—ear, leg, or bunch of hair," slip the harness over the dog's head, push his front legs through, and tie him to a rock. Finally, Matt said, he would lick his dog bites.

When the dogs were in their traces, they spread out like a fan in front of the sledge. The king dog, who was the strongest and fiercest, led the way in the center. Matt had watched the Eskimos drive the dogs and knew that they

Dogs in their traces fan out in front of a sledge. If they are starving,
the dogs will eat their traces, which are made of sealskin.

didn't use the 30-foot sealskin whip *on* the dogs but *over*
the dogs. The trick was to make the whip curl out and crack
like a gunshot right over the ear of the dog who needed it.
Matt stepped up behind the sledge, shouted, "Huk, huk!"
and tried to crack the whip. The dogs sat down. Matt tried
again and again and again. After many tries and lots of help
from his Eskimo teachers, Matt learned how to snap the
whip over the dogs' ears and make them start off at a trot.
Then he had to learn how to turn them (they didn't have
reins, as horses do), how to make them stop, and how to
make them jump over open water with the sledge flying
behind.

There were five Eskimo families at the camp, each family with its own stone igloo. At first it was hard for Matt to go inside the igloos because of their peculiar smell (Eskimos did not take baths, and Matt said that an Eskimo mother cleans her baby just as a mother cat cleans her kittens), but he didn't want to be rude, so he got used to it. Opposite the entrance hole was the bed platform, built of stone and covered with furs. At the end of the bed platform was a small stone lamp, filled with whale blubber for fuel, with moss for the wick. This little lamp was the light and heat and cook stove for the igloo. The Eskimo woman melted snow in a small pan over the lamp and used the water for cooking meat and for drinking. (Eskimos did not build fires for heating or cooking.)

Matt learned how to build a snow igloo when he hunted with the Eskimos, far from the camp. Two Eskimos could cut 50 to 60 snow blocks (each block 6-by-18-by-24-inches) with their long snow knives and build a whole igloo in just one hour. One man would stand in the center and place the blocks in an 8-foot circle around himself. He would add more blocks, spiraling round and round, with the blocks closing in on the center as they rose higher, until the top snow blocks fit perfectly against each other and the roof was complete. Then they would carry in the furs and cooking lamp, and it was home. A chunk of frozen meat, perhaps part of a walrus, might be in the middle of the igloo, handy for snacks and also a good footstool. Snow igloos even had shelves. The Eskimos would stick their

Dogs curl up outside Peary's igloo.

snowshoes into the wall and lay mittens on the snowshoe shelf to dry.

The dogs, who had thick silver gray or white hair with a layer of short fine fur underneath to keep them warm, lived outdoors in the snow. They would curl into balls, cover their noses with their tails, and sleep, warm as muffins (usually), even if it was -50°F.

During the full moons Matt and the Eskimos hunted reindeer and arctic hares. The large pure white hares themselves could not be seen against the white snow, only their black shadows. They were like an army of frozen or leaping ghosts. And in the deep blackness of the arctic night, Matt saw hundreds of shooting stars, so thick and close they seemed to burst like rockets. While he watched the stars, the Eskimos explained that what Matt called the Big Dipper was really seven reindeer eating grass, and the constellation he called the Pleiades was really a team of dogs chasing a polar bear.

The Eskimos had no tables or chairs, no books or paper or writing, no money or bills to pay, no king or chief, no doctors or dentists, no schools or churches, no laws, and no wars. They needed shelter from the cold, strong dogs to pull their sledges, and animals they could hunt for furs and meat. Several families usually lived close together to help each other. If one man killed a walrus, he would share it with everyone. Perhaps in a few days another man would kill a bear or a reindeer; then that man would share it too.

Meanwhile in the wooden house, there was more to eat than raw meat, and there was a new cook. Mrs. Peary wrote in her diary for November 17, 1891, "Matt got supper tonight, and will from now until May 1 prepare all the meals under my supervision." For Christmas, at least, he didn't do all the cooking. Mrs. Peary prepared arctic hare pie with green peas, reindeer with cranberry sauce, corn and tomatoes, plum pudding, and apricot pie. Then, wrote Mrs. Peary, "Matt cleared everything away."

In February the sun returned. For days and days before it actually appeared, the sky was a magnificent dawn of pink, blue, crimson, and deep yellow, with rosy clouds. Then the sun appeared in the south at noon, but just for a moment the first day. Each day it rose a little higher. The crystal clear water in the bay was deep blue, and the air was thick with the sound of wings and songs as thousands of birds swooped and swarmed over the water and up the cliffs.

But Greenland's ice cap, which Matt intended to cross, was a frozen, lifeless desert of snow and howling wind and glaciers and deep crevasses. Even though Matt always covered the inside of his boots with soft dried moss for insulation, his heel froze when he helped haul boxes of pemmican and biscuits up to the ice cap in the beginning of May. (Freezing is very serious. The blood stops moving in the frozen part, and the skin and muscle can soon die.) Matt, who was the best at driving the dogs and at speaking the Eskimo language, had planned to be one of the first men to cross the ice cap, but Peary sent him back to the base camp. There were three reasons: one was the frozen heel; another was that someone had to protect Mrs. Peary at the camp; and the third was that Peary believed an explorer should have a college education in order to know what to do in an emergency.

During the short summer, while the others were gone, Matt went hunting so everyone would have plenty of fresh meat; he learned more of the Eskimo language; his foot healed; and he protected Mrs. Peary from danger.

In the end only Peary and Astrup actually crossed the ice cap. All the others turned back. The Eskimos, who feared Kokoyah, the evil spirit of the ice cap, refused to go at all. Peary did discover a large bay at the northeast corner of Greenland, which he named Independence Bay, but he did not find out if there was a way to get to the North Pole by land. He would have to try again. He asked Matt to come along again too.

NACHITO'S TEACHINGS

from MEDICINE WALK
by Ardath Mayhar
illustrated by Amanda Welch

*While flying over the Arizona desert, Burr's father
has a heart attack. The plane crashes, leaving Burr forty
miles from safety and alone. Burr must now rely on his will
to survive and the teachings of Nachito, a former Apache
farmhand, to overcome the dangers of the desert.*

The morning was hot. The air was thin and dry, and
the sky was a faded blue that promised no relief. I
had spent my first night huddled into a cranny in
another of the dry washes that seemed to runnel the whole
area. I'd been as cold then as I was hot now. There was a
hogback ridge ahead. Again. I seemed to do nothing but
climb up or climb down. I was one huge ache. A dry ache.

I was thirsty . . . more than thirsty, but I didn't touch the
bottle. I wasn't doing so well as those old Apache, not by a
long shot. I had taken a mouthful early and maybe traveled
a mile before I swallowed it. I hoped to do a lot better next

time. Just having water in my mouth helped a lot. It held off the raspy-throated feeling; my tongue didn't behave like used sandpaper. At noon I'd take another mouthful and try to hold it half the afternoon. If I could.

I was moving carefully, checking for loose rock and unexpected holes. A broken leg would mean the end, out here. Still, even that was getting to be automatic, and my mind kept wandering off, spinning strange notions.

Mom drifted out of a clump of rock up ahead. She was wearing the blue jumpsuit she liked best. In her hands was a glass of lemonade. "Hurry, Burr! It'll get warm before you drink it!" she was urging me. I could see her bronze hair

moving in the breeze. Her bandana, stuck in her hip pocket, was fluttering, too.

I almost let go and ran to her, but I caught myself. That wasn't here and now. That was the morning of the awful day. I had run, then, grabbed the glass and gulped down the liquid. She'd tousled my hair with her strong fingers and said, "Want to go with me, old chum? It's going to be an exciting show, and your Aunt Martha would love for you to be there."

I had grinned at her over the rim of the glass. "Yeah. I know how much she likes my comments on her paintings. Thanks, Mom, but no thanks. I like pictures, but I hate fine art. Or maybe I just don't like the kind of people who go to things like that. I'd rather stay here and go scavenging with Charlie."

She had laughed, that deep chuckle that always made me feel good inside. "I don't really blame you. The arty ones turn me off, too. But Martha would be hurt if I didn't show up. Have fun, and don't get snakebit!"

I hadn't even kissed her goodbye. That still rankled, deep down inside where nobody knew it but me. And before she got to town a truck creamed her little sports car.

I shook my head hard and came to, standing on the rocky slope. I didn't need that kind of thing. I had to keep my mind on what I was doing, not go wandering around in a daze, daydreaming. That was a good way to get killed, and I knew it all too well.

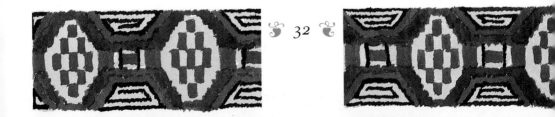

At noon I paused on top of a ridge. There was a stunted piñon growing there, and I thought of something Nachito had told me. I pulled a handful of the fragrant needles and tucked them into my pocket. One I put into my mouth and chewed. The acid taste made my mouth water, which was all to the good. A cheap drink, though not very satisfying. Still, it was enough to let me swallow a small pinch of raisins and half an apricot. I left the bottle untouched. It was a matter of pride, now.

I angled down the other side of the ridge. Its twin loomed ahead, and I groaned. All the relatives who had visited us had raved over the mountains in Arizona. It was sure and certain that they hadn't had to walk over them. Not only was it exhausting, but I was having trouble keeping directions straight in my head, what with all the going up and down and back and forth, finding passable places. I must have traveled twelve or fifteen miles since I set out, but I probably hadn't gone more than five miles east. If that.

I lucked into a game trail about halfway down the ridge. It meandered among the rocky ledges, but it was better than trying to find a way down the steep slope with no guide at all. I was stepping along, half in a dream again and fussing at myself about it, when I heard a buzzing rattle.

I froze. Where was it? I turned my eyeballs in their sockets, not moving anything else. Right to left. Back again. There! Up ahead, its dusty colors hiding it against the baked rock and dust of the trail, was a diamond-back. Its

head was forward, forked tongue testing the air. Its tail was quivering furiously.

I hate snakes. I'm not exactly afraid of them; something in my inside just squirms when I see the way they move. But I was afraid of this one. To be bitten, out here alone, would be bad. Fatally bad.

Something popped into my mind. Charlie handled snakes. Live ones, rattlers and all. He had never been bitten. Nachito trained Charlie. I often overheard their conversations. What was it Nachito had told him? I could see the seamed, saddle-colored face, the narrow squinted eyes, as the old man oiled harness leather and talked, while we polished bits and stirrups.

"The snake, he is a part of the land. He is wise, in his own way, and he is dangerous, for he knows only his own way. A man knows more than a snake. He can cow a snake, if he doesn't smell of fear. A serpent knows one thing: a fearful man is dangerous to him. He will strike if he smells fear on you. But if you are not afraid . . . not a little bit . . . you can calm him. You can make him wonder, deep in that small, strange brain, what it is that you are and can do. And then you are the winner."

That had been something Nachito had worked out for himself, I thought, for none of the Apache hands seemed to know about it. But it sounded as if it might be true. Nachito usually knew what he was talking about.

I stared at the long, coiled shape. I made myself relax, muscle by muscle, without moving a peg. My nerves quit

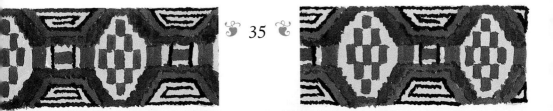

jumping and lay quiet. My breathing eased. My hands unclenched. The snake's head lowered to a point just above the first coil. The buzz changed its pitch.

The diamond-back wasn't a horrible-looking creature, once you thought about it. It was beautiful, in its own way. Strong and sleek, patterned in subdued colors just right for its world. And the poison; it was no worse than my own ability to pick up a stick and smash the creature flat.

I looked into the serpent's eyes. It lowered its head even more. I didn't blink, but set my will against that of the snake. I urged it with all my might to go on about its business among the rocks. The rattle rasped irritably.

Time crawled past. The sun moved slowly down toward the top of the ridge high above, though I didn't spare much thought for it. And at last the snake began uncoiling. It curled its head about as if looking for a direction. I willed harder than ever, sweat pouring off me—from the sun, now, not from fear. And the rattler slid away among the rocks.

My knees felt weak. My heart was pounding, but not with fear. I'd been working harder, those past minutes, than ever before in my life. And I'd won! A feeling of triumph swept over me. Nachito had been right! And I'd been able to use his words to make myself unafraid. If I could do this much, maybe I just might make it!

My head was light with relief when I went on. The trail eased down, into the cooler bowl of shadow that was the eastern slope of the ridge, safe now from the sun. I picked up my pace as the going grew easier.

I smelled water!

Between the ridge I'd just come down and the toes of the neighboring mesa ran a narrow valley. At its bottom there was a wide streambed with a trickle of water snaking down its middle. Cottonwoods were growing along the banks, and scrub and a few piñons lined its course.

I badly wanted to run the rest of the way. But I'd been walking over this kind of terrain for a while now. I knew the sort of trap it could set for a foot that wasn't very careful. I held myself back by main force, but I did fumble for the water bottle and drain it into my mouth.

Something inside me perked up to attention. "That was a foolish thing," it said to me, almost in a real voice. "What if the water down there is alky-water? What if it's polluted so you can't drink it? What'll you do then? And now you've spoiled your control. You'll have to start all over again."

It wasn't exactly me talking, way down there inside myself. It was partly Nachito's teachings, partly my listening to the tales the Apache hands told and to Charlie's family stories. This wasn't my own country. My kind had never had to face it, raw, the way the Apache had. But the Apache were human beings, no more, no less. What they could learn to do, surely I could—if I had the time left before a rattler or the sun or thirst got me. But I knew how lucky I was to have shared even a little of Charlie's training. It gave me a handle on things that I'd never have been able to work out for myself.

ISLAND OF THE BLUE DOLPHINS

from the book by Scott O'Dell

illustrated by Russ Walks

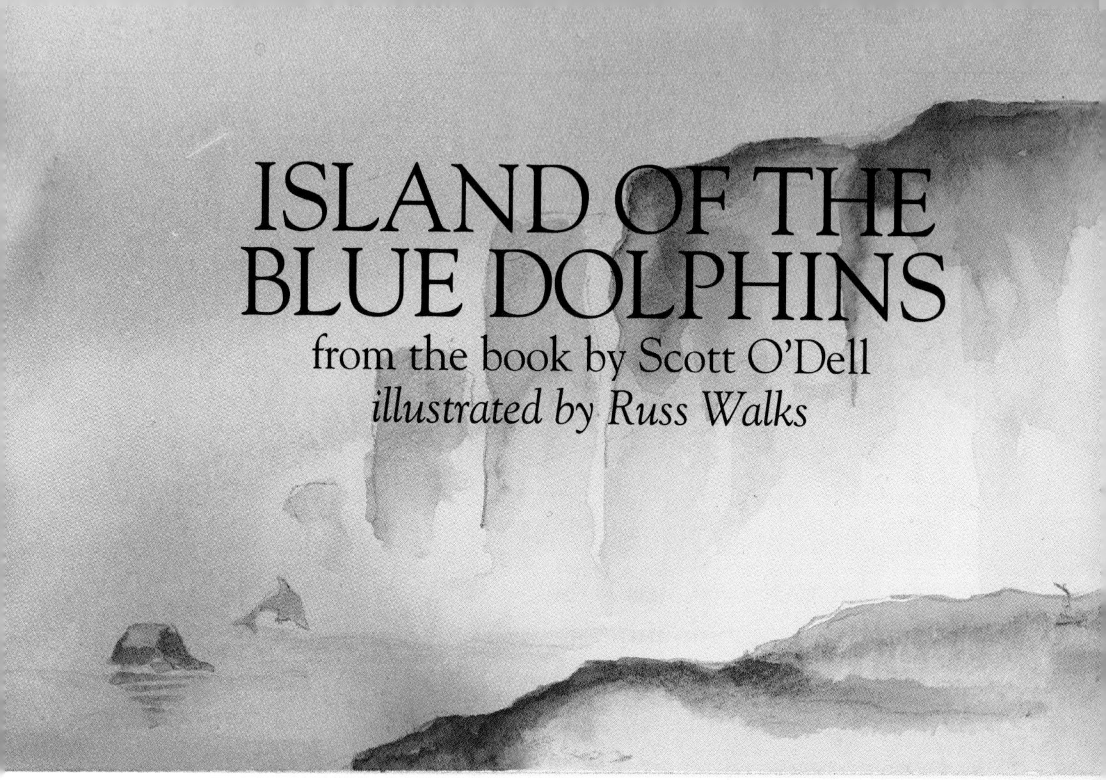

*With the help of the white man's ship, Karana's
people have fled their island to escape the Aleuts, their
enemies. In their haste Karana is accidentally left behind on
the island. As she waits for a ship to return to rescue her,
Karana's hopes begin to fade.*

Summer is the best time on the Island of the Blue Dolphins. The sun is warm then and the winds blow milder out of the west, sometimes out of the south.

It was during these days that the ship might return and now I spent most of my time on the rock, looking out from the high headland into the east, toward the country where my people had gone, across the sea that was never-ending.

Once while I watched I saw a small object which I took to be the ship, but a stream of water rose from it and I knew that it was a whale spouting. During those summer days I saw nothing else.

The first storm of winter ended my hopes. If the white men's ship were coming for me it would have come during the time of good weather. Now I would have to wait until winter was gone, maybe longer.

The thought of being alone on the island while so many suns rose from the sea and went slowly back into the sea filled my heart with loneliness. I had not felt so lonely before because I was sure that the ship would return as Matasaip had said it would. Now my hopes were dead. Now I was really alone. I could not eat much, nor could I sleep without dreaming terrible dreams.

The storm blew out of the north, sending big waves against the island and winds so strong that I was unable to stay on the rock. I moved my bed to the foot of the rock and for protection kept a fire going throughout the night. I slept there five times. The first night the dogs came and stood outside the ring made by the fire. I killed three of them with arrows, but not the leader, and they did not come again.

On the sixth day, when the storm had ended, I went to the place where the canoes had been hidden, and let myself down over the cliff. This part of the shore was sheltered from the wind and I found the canoes just as they had been left. The dried food was still good, but the water was stale, so I went back to the spring and filled a fresh basket.

I had decided during the days of the storm, when I had given up hope of seeing the ship, that I would take one of the canoes and go to the country that lay toward the east. I remembered how Kimki, before he had gone, had asked the advice of his ancestors who had lived many ages in the past, who had come to the island from that country, and likewise the advice of Zuma, the medicine man who held power over the wind and the seas. But these things I could not do, for Zuma had been killed by the Aleuts, and in all my life I had never been able to speak with the dead, though many times I had tried.

Yet I cannot say that I was really afraid as I stood there on the shore. I knew that my ancestors had crossed the sea in their canoes, coming from that place which lay beyond. Kimki, too had crossed the sea. I was not nearly so skilled with a canoe as these men, but I must say that whatever might befall me on the endless waters did not trouble me. It meant far less than the thought of staying on the island alone, without a home or companions, pursued by wild dogs, where everything reminded me of those who were dead and those who had gone away.

Of the four canoes stored there against the cliff, I chose the smallest, which was still very heavy because it could carry six people. The task that faced me was to push it down the rocky shore and into the water, a distance four or five times its length.

This I did by first removing all the large rocks in front of the canoe. I then filled in all these holes with pebbles and

along this path laid down long strips of kelp, making a slippery bed. The shore was steep and once I got the canoe to move with its own weight, it slid down the path and into the water.

The sun was in the west when I left the shore. The sea was calm behind the high cliffs. Using the two-bladed paddle I quickly skirted the south part of the island. As I reached the sandspit the wind struck. I was paddling from the back of the canoe because you can go faster kneeling there, but I could not handle it in the wind.

Kneeling in the middle of the canoe, I paddled hard and did not pause until I had gone through the tides that run fast around the sandspit. There were many small waves and I was soon wet, but as I came out from behind the spit the spray lessened and the waves grew long and rolling. Though it would have been easier to go the way they slanted, this would have taken me in the wrong direction. I therefore kept them on my left hand, as well as the island, which grew smaller and smaller, behind me.

At dusk I looked back. The Island of the Blue Dolphins had disappeared. This was the first time that I felt afraid.

There were only hills and valleys of water around me now. When I was in a valley I could see nothing and when the canoe rose out of it, only the ocean stretching away and away.

Night fell and I drank from the basket. The water cooled my throat.

The sea was black and there was no difference between it and the sky. The waves made no sound among themselves,

only faint noises as they went under the canoe or struck against it. Sometimes the noises seemed angry and at other times like people laughing. I was not hungry because of my fear.

The first star made me feel less afraid. It came out low in the sky and it was in front of me, toward the east. Other stars began to appear all around, but it was this one I kept my gaze upon. It was in the figure that we call a serpent, a star which shone green and which I knew. Now and then it was hidden by mist, yet it always came out brightly again.

Without this star I would have been lost, for the waves never changed. They came always from the same direction and in a manner that kept pushing me away from the place I wanted to reach. For this reason the canoe made a path in the black water like a snake. But somehow I kept moving toward the star which shone in the east.

This star rose high and then I kept the North Star on my left hand, the one we call "the star that does not move." The wind grew quiet. Since it always died down when the night was half over, I knew how long I had been traveling and how far away the dawn was.

About this time I found that the canoe was leaking. Before dark I had emptied one of the baskets in which food was stored and used it to dip out the water that came over the sides. The water that now moved around my knees was not from the waves.

I stopped paddling and worked with the basket until the bottom of the canoe was almost dry. Then I searched around, feeling in the dark along the smooth planks, and found the place near the bow where the water was seeping through a crack as long as my hand and the width of a finger. Most of the time it was out of the sea, but it leaked whenever the canoe dipped forward in the waves.

The places between the planks were filled with black pitch which we gather along the shore. Lacking this, I tore a piece of fiber from my skirt and pressed it into the crack, which held back the water.

Dawn broke in a clear sky and as the sun came out of the waves I saw that it was far off on my left. During the night I had drifted south of the place I wished to go, so I changed my direction and paddled along the path made by the rising sun.

There was no wind on this morning and the long waves went quietly under the canoe. I therefore moved faster than during the night.

I was very tired, but more hopeful than I had been since I left the island. If the good weather did not change I would cover many leagues before dark. Another night and another day might bring me within sight of the shore toward which I was going.

Not long after dawn, while I was thinking of this strange place and what it would look like, the canoe began to leak again. This crack was between the same planks, but was a larger one and close to where I was kneeling.

The fiber I tore from my skirt and pushed into the crack held back most of the water which seeped in whenever the canoe rose and fell with the waves. Yet I could see that the planks were weak from one end to the other, probably from the canoe being stored so long in the sun, and that they might open along their whole length if the waves grew rougher.

It was suddenly clear to me that it was dangerous to go on. The voyage would take two more days, perhaps longer. By turning back to the island I would not have nearly so far to travel.

Still I could not make up my mind to do so. The sea was calm and I had come far. The thought of turning back after all this labor was more than I could bear. Even greater was the thought of the deserted island I would return to, of living there alone and forgotten. For how many suns and how many moons?

The canoe drifted idly on the calm sea while these thoughts went over and over in my mind, but when I saw the water seeping through the crack again, I picked up the paddle. There was no choice except to turn back toward the island.

I knew that only by the best of fortune would I ever reach it.

The wind did not blow until the sun was overhead. Before that time I covered a good distance, pausing only when it was necessary to dip water from the canoe. With the wind I went more slowly and had to stop more often because of the water spilling over the sides, but the leak did not grow worse.

This was my first good fortune. The next was when a swarm of dolphins appeared. They came swimming out of the west, but as they saw the canoe they turned around in a great circle and began to follow me. They swam up slowly and so close that I could see their eyes, which are large and the color of the ocean. Then they swam on ahead of the canoe, crossing back and forth in front of it, diving in and out, as if they were weaving a piece of cloth with their broad snouts.

Dolphins are animals of good omen. It made me happy to have them swimming around the canoe, and though my hands had begun to bleed from the chafing of the paddle, just watching them made me forget the pain. I was very lonely before they appeared, but now I felt that I had friends with me and did not feel the same.

The blue dolphins left me shortly before dusk. They left as quickly as they had come, going on into the west, but for a long time I could see the last of the sun shining on them. After night fell I could still see them in my thoughts and it was because of this that I kept on paddling when I wanted to lie down and sleep.

More than anything, it was the blue dolphins that took me back home.

Fog came with the night, yet from time to time I could see the star that stands high in the west, the red star called Magat which is part of the figure that looks like a crawfish and is known by that name. The crack in the planks grew wider so I had to stop often to fill it with fiber and to dip out the water.

The night was very long, longer than the night before. Twice I dozed kneeling there in the canoe, though I was more afraid than I had ever been. But the morning broke clear and in front of me lay the dim line of the island like a great fish sunning itself on the sea.

I reached it before the sun was high, the sandspit and its tides that bore me into the shore. My legs were stiff from kneeling and as the canoe struck the sand I fell when I rose to climb out. I crawled through the shallow water and up the beach. There I lay for a long time, hugging the sand in happiness.

I was too tired to think of the wild dogs. Soon I fell asleep.

MEET SCOTT O'DELL, AUTHOR

"Island of the Blue Dolphins *is based upon the true story of a girl who was left upon an island near the coast of Southern California and lived there for eighteen years, alone.*" *Scott O'Dell describes how he developed the idea for this book:* "It came directly from the memory of the years I lived at Rattlesnake Island and San Pedro (in Southern California). Places I have known, creatures I have loved are in* Island of the Blue Dolphins. *The islands seen at dawn and at sunset, in all weathers over many years. Dolphin and otter playing. A mother gull pushing her brood from the nest. And finally there is Carolina, who lived in central Mexico. When she first came to work for us, she wore a long red skirt of closely woven wool. She wore it proudly, as a shield against the world, in the way Karana (the heroine of* Island of the Blue Dolphins) *wore the skirt of cormorant feathers.*"

McBROOM AND THE BIG WIND

Sid Fleischman
illustrated by Walter Lorraine

I can't deny it—it does get a mite windy out here on the
prairie. Why, just last year a blow came ripping across
our farm and carried off a pail of sweet milk. The next
day it came back for the cow.

But that wasn't the howlin', scowlin', almighty *big* wind I
aim to tell you about. That was just a common little prairie
breeze. No account, really. Hardly worth bragging about.

It was the *big* wind that broke my leg. I don't expect you
to believe that—yet. I'd best start with some smaller
weather and work up to that bonebreaker.

I remember distinctly the first prairie wind that came
scampering along after we bought our wonderful one-acre
farm. My, that land is rich. Best topsoil in the country.
There isn't a thing that won't grow in our rich topsoil, and
fast as lightning.

The morning I'm talking about our oldest boys were helping me to shingle the roof. I had bought a keg of nails, but it turned out those nails were a whit short. We buried them in our wonderful topsoil and watered them down. In five or ten minutes those nails grew a full half-inch.

So there we were, up on the roof, hammering down shingles. There wasn't a cloud in the sky at first. The younger boys were shooting marbles all over the farm and the girls were jumping rope.

When I had pounded down the last shingle I said to myself, "Josh McBroom, that's a mighty stout roof. It'll last a hundred years."

Just then I felt a small draft on the back of my neck. A moment later one of the girls—it was Polly, as I recall—shouted up to me. "Pa," she said, "do jackrabbits have wings?"

I laughed. "No, Polly."

"Then how come there's a flock of jackrabbits flying over the house?"

I looked up. Mercy! Rabbits were flapping their ears across the sky in a perfect V formation, northbound. I knew then we were in for a slight blow.

"Run, everybody!" I shouted to the young'uns. I didn't want the wind picking them up by the ears. "Will*jill*-hester*chester*peter*polly*tim*tom*mary*larry*andlittle*clarinda*—in the house! Scamper!"

The clothesline was already beginning to whip around like a jump rope. My dear wife, Melissa, who had been baking a heap of biscuits, threw open the door. In we dashed and not a moment too soon. The wind was snapping at our heels like a pack of wolves. It aimed to barge right in and make itself at home! A prairie wind has no manners at all.

We slammed the door in its teeth. Now, the wind didn't take that politely. It rammed and battered at the door while all of us pushed and shoved to hold the door shut. My, it was a battle! How the house creaked and trembled!

"Push, my lambs!" I yelled. "Shove!"

At times the door planks bent like barrel staves. But we held that roaring wind out. When it saw there was no getting past us, the zephyr sneaked around the house to the back door. However, our oldest boy, Will, was too smart for it. He piled Mama's heap of fresh biscuits against the back door. My dear wife, Melissa, is a wonderful cook, but her biscuits *are* terribly heavy. They made a splendid door stop.

But what worried me most was our wondrous rich topsoil. That thieving wind was apt to make off with it, leaving us with a trifling hole in the ground.

"Shove, my lambs!" I said. "Push!"

The battle raged on for an hour. Finally the wind gave up butting its fool head against the door. With a great angry sigh it turned and whisked itself away, scattering fence pickets as it went.

We all took a deep breath and I opened the door a crack. Hardly a leaf now stirred on the ground. A bird began to twitter. I rushed outside to our poor one-acre farm.

Mercy! What I saw left me popeyed. "Melissa!" I shouted with glee. "Will*jill*hester*chester*peter*polly*tim*tom*mary*larry*-andlittle*clarinda!* Come here, my lambs! Look!"

We all gazed in wonder. Our topsoil was still there—every bit. Bless those youngsters! The boys had left their marbles all over the field, and the marbles had grown as large as boulders. There they sat, huge agates and sparkling

glassies, holding down our precious topsoil.

But that rambunctious wind didn't leave empty-handed. It ripped off our new shingle roof. Pulled out the nails, too. We found out later the wind had shingled every gopher hole in the next county.

Now that was a strong draft. But it wasn't a *big* wind. Nothing like the kind that broke my leg. Still, that prairie gust was an education to me.

"Young'uns," I said, after we'd rolled those giant marbles down the hill. "The next uninvited breeze that comes

along, we'll be ready for it. There are two sides to every flapjack. It appears to me the wind can be downright useful on our farm if we let it know who's boss."

The next gusty day that came along, we put it to work for us. I made a wind plow. I rigged a bedsheet and tackle to our old farm plow. Soon as a breeze sprung up I'd go tacking to and fro over the farm, plowing as I went. Our son Chester once plowed the entire farm in under three minutes.

On Thanksgiving morning Mama told the girls to pluck a large turkey for dinner. They didn't much like that chore, but a prairie gust arrived just in time. The girls stuck the turkey out the window. The wind plucked that turkey clean, pinfeathers and all.

Oh, we got downright glad to see a blow come along. The young'uns were always wanting to go out and play in the wind, but Mama was afraid they'd be carried off. So I made them wind shoes—made 'em out of heavy iron skillets. Out in the breeze those shoes felt light as feathers. The girls would jump rope with the clothesline. The wind spun the rope, of course.

Many a time I saw the youngsters put on their wind shoes and go clumping outside with a big tin funnel and all the empty bottles and jugs they could round up. They'd cork the containers jam full of prairie wind.

Then, come summer, when there wasn't a breath of air, they'd uncork a bottle or two of fresh winter wind and enjoy the cool breeze.

Of course, we had to windproof the farm every fall. We'd plant the field in buttercups. My, they were slippery—all that butter, I guess. The wind would slip and slide over the farm without being able to get a purchase on the topsoil. By then the boys and I had reshingled the roof. We used screws instead of nails.

Mercy! Then came the *big* wind!

It started out gently enough. There were a few jackrabbits and some crows flying backward through the air. Nothing out of the ordinary.

Of course the girls went outside to jump the clothesline and the boys got busy laying up bottles of wind for summer. Mama had just baked a batch of fresh biscuits. My, they did smell good! I ate a dozen or so hot out of the oven. And that turned out to be a terrible mistake.

Outside, the wind was picking up ground speed and scattering fence posts as it went.

"*Willjillhesterchesterpeterpollytimtommarylarryandlittleclarinda!*" I shouted. "Inside, my lambs! That wind is getting ornery!"

The young'uns came trooping in and pulled off their wind shoes. And not a moment too soon. The clothesline began to whip around so fast it seemed to disappear. Then we saw a hen house come flying through the air, with the hens still in it.

The sky was turning dark and mean. The wind came out of the far north, howling and shrieking and shaking the house. In the cupboard, cups chattered in their saucers.

Soon we noticed big balls of fur rolling along the prairie like tumbleweeds. Turned out they were timber wolves from up north. And then an old hollow log came spinning across the farm and split against my chopping stump. Out rolled a black bear, and was he in a temper! He had been trying to hibernate and didn't take kindly to being awakened. He gave out a roar and looked around for

somebody to chase. He saw us at the windows and decided we would do.

The mere sight of him scared the young'uns and they huddled together, holding hands, near the fireplace.

I got down my shotgun and opened a window. That was a *mistake*! Two things happened at once. The bear was coming on and in my haste I forgot to calculate the direction of the wind. It came shrieking along the side of the house and when I poked the gunbarrel out the window, well, the wind bent it like an angle iron. That buckshot flew due south. I found out later it brought down a brace of ducks over Mexico.

But worse than that, when I threw open the window such a draft came in that our young'uns *were sucked up through the chimney*! Holding hands, they were carried away like a string of sausages.

Mama near fainted away. "My dear Melissa," I exclaimed. "Don't you worry! I'll get our young'uns back!"

I fetched a rope and rushed outside. I could see the
young'uns up in the sky and blowing south.

I could also see the bear and he could see me. He gave
a growl with a mouthful of teeth like rusty nails. He rose
up on his hind legs and came toward me with his eyes
glowing red as fire.

I didn't fancy tangling with that monster. I dodged
around behind the clothesline. I kept one eye on the bear
and the other on the young'uns. They were now flying
over the county seat and looked hardly bigger than
mayflies.

The bear charged toward me. The wind was spinning
the clothesline so fast he couldn't see it. And he charged
smack into it. My, didn't he begin to jump! He jumped
red-hot pepper, only faster. He
had got himself trapped inside
the rope and couldn't jump out.

Of course, I didn't lose a
moment. I began flapping my
arms like a bird. That was such
an enormous *big* wind I figured I
could fly after the young'uns.
The wind tugged and pulled at
me, but it couldn't lift me an
inch off the ground.

Tarnation! I had eaten too many biscuits. They were heavy as lead and weighed me down.

The young'uns were almost out of sight. I rushed to the barn for the wind plow. Once out in the breeze, the bedsheet filled with wind. Off I shot like a cannonball, plowing a deep furrow as I went.

Didn't I streak along, though! I was making better time than the young'uns. I kept my hands on the plow handles and steered around barns and farmhouses. I saw haystacks explode in the wind. If that wind got any stronger it wouldn't surprise me to see the sun blown off course. It would set in the south at high noon.

I plowed right along and gained rapidly on the young'uns. They were still holding hands and just clearing the tree tops. Before long I was within hailing distance.

"Be brave, my lambs!" I shouted. "Hold tight!"

I spurted after them until their shadows lay across my path. But the bedsheet was so swelled out with wind that I couldn't stop the plow. Before I could let go of the handles and jump off I had sailed far *ahead* of the young'uns.

I heaved the rope into the air. "Will*jill*hester*chester*peter-*polly*timtommary*larry*and*little*clarinda!" I shouted as they came flying overhead. "Hang on!"

Hester missed the rope, and Jill missed the rope, and so did Peter. But Will caught it. I had to dig my heels in the earth to hold them. And then I started back. The young'uns were too light for the wind. They hung in the air. I had to drag them home on the rope like balloons on a string.

Of course it took most of the day to shoulder my way back through the wind. It was a mighty struggle, I tell you! It was near suppertime when we saw our farmhouse ahead, and that black bear was still jumping rope!

I dragged the young'uns into the house. The rascals! They had had a jolly time flying through the air, and wanted to do it again! Mama put them to bed with their wind shoes on.

The wind blew all night, and the next morning that bear was still jumping rope. His tongue was hanging out and he had lost so much weight he was skin and bones.

Finally, about midmorning, the wind got tired of blowing one way, so it blew the other. We got to feeling sorry for that bear and cut him loose. He was so tuckered out he didn't even growl. He just pointed himself toward the tall timber to find another hollow log to crawl into. But he had lost the fine art of walking. We watched him jump, jump, jump north until he was out of sight.

That was the howlin', scowlin' all mighty *big* wind that broke my leg. It had not only pulled up fence posts, but the *holes* as well. It dropped one of these holes right outside the barn door and I stepped in it.

That's the bottom truth. Everyone on the prairie knows Josh McBroom would rather break his leg than tell a fib.

MEET SID FLEISCHMAN, AUTHOR

Sid Fleischman has written several funny books about the McBroom character. He states: "I am a strong advocate of humor in children's books. It amazes me that I have written ten McBroom tall tales . . . It was never my intention to go beyond the first book (McBroom Tells the Truth), but a new idea seems to crop up every year or so. I tell myself that each new McBroom tale is positively the last—until the next irresistible idea makes a liar of me."

THE GRASSHOPPER

David McCord
illustrated by Nelle Davis

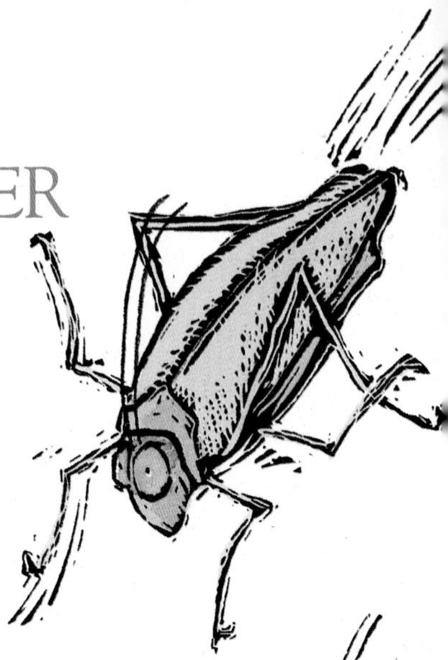

Down
a
deep
well
a
grasshopper
fell.

By kicking about
He thought to get out.
    He might have known better,
    For that got him wetter.

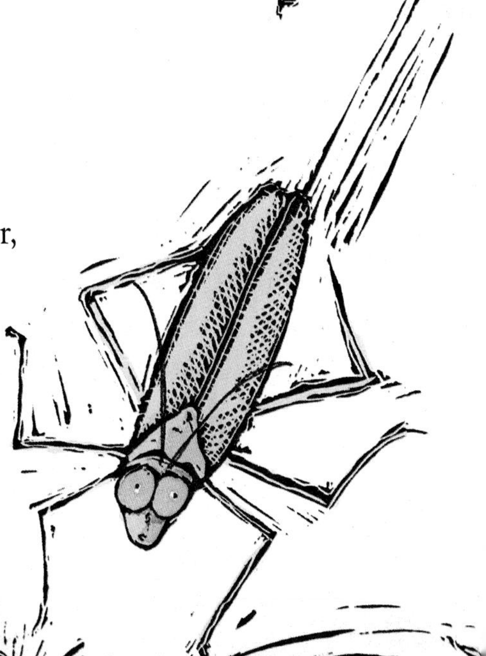

To kick round and round
Is the way to get drowned,
    And drowning is what
    I should tell you he got.

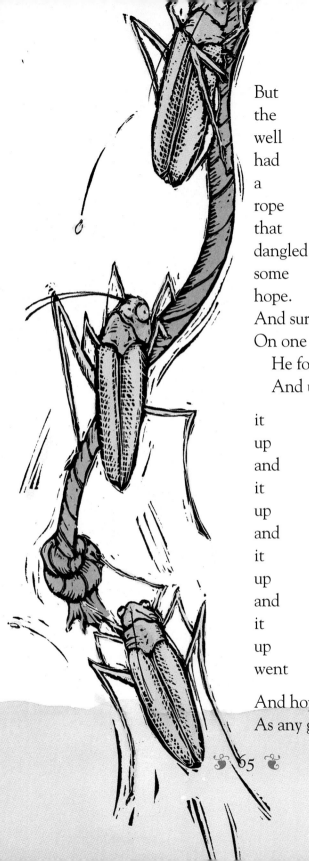

But
the
well
had
a
rope
that
dangled
some
hope.
And sure as molasses
On one of his passes
   He found the rope handy
    And up he went, *and he*

it
up
and
it
up
and
it
up
and
it
up
went

And hopped away proper
As any grasshopper.

❧ 65 ❧

THE BIG WAVE

Pearl S. Buck

illustrated by Yoriko Ito

津波

Jiya and his family live in a small Japanese fishing village. When a distant volcano erupts, it causes a tidal wave. As the giant wave approaches the village, Jiya's father forces him to climb to safety on a nearby mountain. He climbs to the terraced farm of his friend Kino's family. The rest of Jiya's family stays behind. From the mountaintop, Jiya watches as the wave hits.

Upon the beach where the village stood not a house remained, no wreckage of wood or fallen stone wall, no little street of shops, no docks, not a single boat. The beach was as clean of houses as if no human beings had ever lived there. All that had been was now no more.

Jiya gave a wild cry and Kino felt him slip to the ground. He was unconscious. What he had seen was too much for him. What he knew, he could not bear. His family and his home were gone.

Kino began to cry and Kino's father did not stop him. He stooped and gathered Jiya into his arms and carried him into the house, and Kino's mother ran out of the kitchen and put down a mattress and Kino's father laid Jiya upon it.

"It is better that he is unconscious," he said gently. "Let him remain so until his own will wakes him. I will sit by him."

"I will rub his hands and feet," Kino's mother said sadly.

Kino could say nothing. He was still crying and his father let him cry for a while. Then he said to his wife:

"Heat a little rice soup for Kino and put some ginger in it. He feels cold."

Now Kino did not know until his father spoke that he did feel cold. He was shivering and he could not stop crying. Setsu came in. She had not seen the big wave, for her mother had closed the windows and drawn the curtains against the sea. But now she saw Jiya lying white-pale and still.

"Is Jiya dead?" she asked.

"No, Jiya is living," her father replied.

"Why doesn't he open his eyes?" she asked again.

"Soon he will open his eyes," the father replied.

"If Jiya is not dead, why does Kino cry?" Setsu asked.

"You are asking too many questions," her father told her. "Go back to the kitchen and help your mother."

So Setsu went back again, sucking her forefinger, and staring at Jiya and Kino as she went, and soon the mother came in with the hot rice soup and Kino drank it. He felt warm now and he could stop crying. But he was still frightened and sad.

"What will we say to Jiya when he wakes?" he asked his father.

"We will not talk," his father replied. "We will give him warm food and let him rest. We will help him to feel he still has a home."

"Here?" Kino asked.

"Yes," his father replied. "I have always wanted another son, and Jiya will be that son. As soon as he knows that this is his home, then we must help him to understand what has happened."

So they waited for Jiya to wake.

"I don't think Jiya can ever be happy again," Kino said sorrowfully.

"Yes, he will be happy someday," his father said, "for life is always stronger than death. Jiya will feel when he wakes that he can never be happy again. He will cry and cry and we must let him cry. But he cannot always cry. After a few days he will stop crying all the time. He will cry only part of the time. He will sit sad and quiet. We must allow him to be sad and we must not make him speak. But we will do our work and live as always we do. Then one day he will be hungry and he will eat something that our mother cooks, something special, and he will begin to feel better. He will not cry any more in the daytime but only at night. We must let him cry at night. But all the time his body will be renewing itself. His blood flowing in his veins, his growing bones, his mind beginning to think again, will make him live."

"He cannot forget his father and mother and his brother!" Kino exclaimed.

"He cannot and he should not forget them," Kino's father said. "Just as he lived with them alive, he will live with them dead. Someday he will accept their death as part of his life. He will weep no more. He will carry them in his memory and his thoughts. His flesh and blood are part of them. So long as he is alive, they, too, will live in him. The big wave came, but it went away. The sun shines again, birds sing, and earth flowers. Look out over the sea now!"

お父さん
じゃは
大丈夫
なの。

よりこ

❧ 69 ❧

Kino looked out the open door, and he saw the ocean sparkling and smooth. The sky was blue again, a few clouds on the horizon were the only sign of what had passed—except for the empty beach.

"How cruel it seems for the sky to be so clear and the ocean so calm!" Kino said.

But his father shook his head. "No, it is wonderful that after the storm the ocean grows calm, and the sky is blue once more. It was not the ocean or the sky that made the evil storm."

"Who made it?" Kino asked. He let tears roll down his cheeks, because there was so much he could not understand. But only his father saw them and his father understood.

"Ah, no one knows who makes evil storms," his father replied. "We only know that they come. When they come we must live through them as bravely as we can, and after they are gone, we must feel again how wonderful is life. Every day of life is more valuable now than it was before the storm."

"But Jiya's family—his father and mother and brother, and all the other good fisherfolk, who are lost—" Kino whispered. He could not forget the dead.

"Now we must think of Jiya," his father reminded him. "He will open his eyes at any minute and we must be there, you to be his brother, and I to be his father. Call your mother, too, and little Setsu."

Now they heard something. Jiya's eyes were still closed, but he was sobbing in his sleep. Kino ran to fetch his mother and Setsu and they gathered about his bed, kneeling on the floor so as to be near Jiya when he opened his eyes.

In a few minutes, while they all watched, Jiya's eyelids fluttered on his pale cheeks, and then he opened his eyes. He did not know where he was. He looked from one face to the other, as though they were strangers. Then he looked up into the beams of the ceiling and around the white walls of the room. He looked at the blue-flowered quilt that covered him.

None of them said anything. They continued to kneel about him, waiting. But Setsu could not keep quiet. She clapped her hands and laughed. "Oh, Jiya has come back!" she cried. "Jiya, did you have a good dream?"

The sound of her voice made him fully awake. "My father—my mother—" he whispered.

Kino's mother took his hand. "I will be your mother now, dear Jiya," she said.

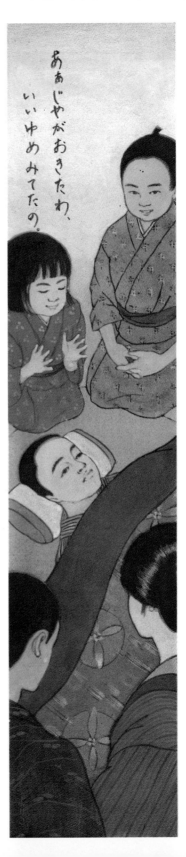

"I will be your father," Kino's father said.

"I am your brother now, Jiya," Kino faltered.

"Oh, Jiya will live with us," Setsu said joyfully.

Then Jiya understood. He got up from the bed and walked to the door that stood open to the sky and the sea. He looked down the hillside to the beach where the fishing village had stood. There was only beach, and all that remained of the twenty and more houses were a few foundation posts and some big stones. The gentle little waves of the ocean were playfully carrying the light timber that had made the houses, and throwing it on the sands and snatching it away again.

The family had followed Jiya and now they stood about him. Kino did not know what to say, for his heart ached for his friend-brother. Kino's mother was wiping her eyes, and even little Setsu looked sad. She took Jiya's hand and stroked it.

"Jiya, I will give you my pet duck," she said.

But Jiya could not speak. He kept on looking at the ocean.

"Jiya, your rice broth is growing cold," Kino's father said.

"We ought all to eat something," Kino's mother said. "I have a fine chicken for dinner."

"I'm hungry!" Setsu cried.

"Come, my son," Kino's father said to Jiya.

They persuaded him gently, gathering around him, and they entered the house again. In the pleasant cosy room they all sat down about the table.

Jiya sat with the others. He was awake, he could hear the voices of Kino's family, and he knew that Kino sat beside him. But inside he still felt asleep. He was very tired, so tired that he did not want to speak. He knew that he would never see his father and mother any more, or his brother, or the neighbors and friends of the village. He tried not to think about them or to imagine their quiet bodies, floating under the swelling waves.

"Eat, Jiya," Kino whispered. "The chicken is good."

Jiya's bowl was before him, untouched. He was not hungry. But when Kino begged him he took up his porcelain spoon and drank a little of the soup. It was hot and good, and he smelled its fragrance in his nostrils. He drank more and then he took up his chopsticks and ate some of the meat and rice. His mind was still unable to think, but his body was young and strong and glad of the food.

When they had all finished, Kino said, "Shall we go up the hillside, Jiya?"

さあじゃ食べて
鶏肉おいしいよ。

But Jiya shook his head. "I want to go to sleep again," he said.

Kino's father understood. "Sleep is good for you," he said. And he led Jiya to his bed, and when Jiya had laid himself down he covered him with the quilt and shut the sliding panels.

"Jiya is not ready yet to live," he told Kino. "We must wait."

The body began to heal first, and Kino's father, watching Jiya tenderly, knew that the body would heal the mind and the soul. "Life is stronger than death," he told Kino again and again.

But each day Jiya was still tired. He did not want to think or to remember—he only wanted to sleep. He woke to eat and then to sleep. And when Kino's mother saw this she led him to the bedroom, and Jiya sank each time into the soft mattress spread on the floor in the quiet, clean room. He fell asleep almost at once and Kino's mother covered him and went away.

All through these days Kino did not feel like playing. He worked hard beside his father in the fields. They did not talk much, and neither of them wanted to look at the sea. It was enough to look at the earth, dark and rich beneath their feet.

One evening, Kino climbed the hill behind the farm and looked toward the volcano. The heavy cloud of smoke had long ago gone away, and the sky was always clear now. He felt happier to know that the volcano was no longer angry, and he went down again to the house. On the threshold his father was smoking his usual evening pipe. In the house his mother was giving Setsu her evening bath.

"Is Jiya asleep already?" Kino asked his father.

"Yes, and it is a good thing for him," his father replied. "Sleep will strengthen him, and when he wakes he will be able to think and remember."

"But should he remember such sorrow?" Kino asked.

"Yes," his father replied. "Only when he dares to remember his parents will he be happy again."

They sat together, father and son, and Kino asked still another question. "Father, are we not very unfortunate people to live in Japan?"

"Why do you think so?" his father asked in reply.

"Because the volcano is behind our house and the ocean is in front, and when they work together for evil, to make the earthquake and the big wave, then we are helpless. Always many of us are lost."

"To live in the midst of danger is to know how good life is," his father replied.

"But if we are lost in the danger?" Kino asked anxiously.

"To live in the presence of death makes us brave and strong," Kino's father replied. "That is why our people never fear death. We see it too often and we do not fear it. To die a little later or a little sooner does not matter. But to live bravely, to love life, to see how beautiful the trees are and the mountains, yes, and even the sea, to enjoy work because it produces food for life—in these things we Japanese are a fortunate people. We love life because we live in danger. We do not fear death because we understand that life and death are necessary to each other."

MEET PEARL S. BUCK, AUTHOR

Pearl S. Buck was born in West Virginia in 1892 but grew up in China, where her parents were missionaries. She returned to China after college to teach English, and it was there that she began to write. Like The Big Wave, *most of Buck's stories are set in Asia. She wrote in part to improve understanding between the people of Asia and the United States, drawing on her experiences as a child.*

SOLITUDE

A. A. Milne
illustrated by Yoriko Ito

I have a house where I go
   When there's too many people,
I have a house where I go
   Where no one can be;
I have a house where I go,
Where nobody ever says "No";
Where no one says anything—so
   There is no one but me.

THE CAGE

Ruth Minsky Sender
illustrated by Bill Fricke

WHY?

Written by Riva Minska, Number 55082
Camp Mittelsteine, Germany, January 14, 1945
Translated from the Yiddish
by Ruth Minsky Sender, Free Person,
New York City, U.S.A. 1980

All alone, I stare at the window
Feeling my soul in me cry
Hearing the painful screams of my heart
Calling silently: Why?
Why are your dreams scattered, destroyed?
Why are you put in this cage?
Why is the world silently watching?
Why can't they hear your rage?
Why is the barbed wire holding me prisoner
Blocking to freedom my way?
Why do I still keep waiting and dreaming
Hoping . . . maybe . . . someday . . .
I see above me the snow-covered mountains
Majestic, proud, and high
If like a free bird I could reach their peaks
Maybe from there the world will hear my cry . . .
Why?

*Riva, a young Jewish girl, has been placed in a
Nazi concentration camp during World War II. She is in a
special section with other girls her age. Each day they are
unsure what will happen to them. Many are put to death.
Others starve. But Riva has a special talent that gives them
all hope.*

"I have something for you." I hear a whisper behind me, as we march back from the factory one evening. I turn my head and look straight into Rosa's smiling eyes.

"Rosa. Where have you been?"

"Keep marching, Riva. The guard is looking in our direction."

I have not seen Rosa since that horrible day when poor Faige lost her mind. I have not seen Faige, either. They say she is kept in the tiny sickroom the doctor uses to help those unlucky enough to become sick here. The doctor is a former medical student with compassion for others.

I often wonder what will become of Faige. No one is allowed more than three days in the sickroom. Will they send her to Grossrosen, the death camp?

"Rosa, I have not seen you since . . ." It's hard to speak of that day.

"I know. They put me on the night shift for a while. This is my first day back on days. And I was lucky today. I saw a small pencil on the foreman's desk, and I thought of you." She stops for a moment. "I stole the pencil," she says quickly.

"Rosa!" I whisper, horrified. "I don't want you to be punished because of me. Why didn't you ask your foreman? You said he was a kind man."

"Oh, that one took sick, and the new foreman . . . Well, let's say I could get into more trouble by asking him. Now, make good use of this treasure."

She puts a small pencil in my hand. I press her hand warmly.

"Hey! You, there! Shut your mouths! March faster!" shout the guards.

My heart is so full of joy, their insults cannot touch me. I have a pencil! I want to shout for joy. I have paper! I have friends! I am going to write again.

The head count passes without incident. No one is punished today. I fly back into the barrack and gulp down my soup, all the time touching my pocket. It is still there. I

slip into my bunk. I must write before they shut off the lights. My hands tremble as the pencil tip flows quickly over the brown pieces of paper, the paper collected so carefully by some of the girls in this barrack. I fold them smoothly to form a booklet, a friend.

I am in a daze. I stare at the written words. They are real. They look back at me. I read silently.

Camp Mittelsteine, Germany.
September 23, 1944
Riva Minska, Number 55082

When my tormented heart can't take any more
The grief within rips it apart;
My tears flow freely—they can't be restrained
I reach for my notebook—my friend.
I speak to my friend of my sorrow
I share my anger, my pain.
I speak to my friend of tomorrow
Of a future we'll build once again!
The pillars I build for the future to come,
I knock down and build once again.
I share all my dreams, share my hopes with my friend
Share the pain that is filling my heart.

I feel at ease now.

"Tola," I whisper. "I have a pencil. I wrote a poem, on paper."

Tola jumps up. "Girls! Riva has a pencil! She wrote a poem! Read, Riva! Read!" she shouts, excited.

Heads poke out from the cubicles. Swollen red eyes stare at me, waiting. I feel so small. So scared now.

I read slowly, my voice shaking. " 'When my tormented heart can't take any more . . .' "

Sobs fill the room.

"Riva, you speak for all of us," Tola says softly. "They cannot kill our spirit, our hunger to survive."

Some days I am filled with hope; others, despair takes over. I put my feelings on brown paper bags. I write poems.

On Sundays, if we are lucky and no punishments are given, I visit the girls in the other barracks. I read my poems. Some girls cry, some listen silently.

The cold, gray days of the season add to our hopelessness. Hungry, weak, beaten, we lie on the sacks of straw in our tiny cubicles. The days are so long. The work at the

factory, the buckets of clay at the bunker, so fatiguing. They sap our last strength. It is hard to keep track of the days.

I lie staring at the yellowish rays thrown by the one small light bulb in the room. I feel only emptiness.

From the narrow opening of one of the bunks a head pokes out. Sara, one of the older girls, looks at the barbed-wire fence beyond the tiny barrack window. Softly she says, "Children, it is Hanukkah," more to herself than to anyone there.

Slowly the silence is broken. One by one, from the fifty wooden cubicles lining the walls of the barrack, heads slip out. Eyes open in bewilderment. "Hanukkah already?" Rosa says. "If I had my mama's latkes today . . ." And with tears in her voice, she adds, "If I had my mama today . . ."

Memories of Hanukkahs with mothers, fathers, sisters, brothers start coming back. Memories of another life. A life almost forgotten, of families sitting around tables, singing songs, sharing latkes, lighting candles, retelling the miracle of Hanukkah. The miracle of the brave Maccabees and their fight for the right to live as Jews. Their fight for religious freedom. Memories of Hanukkah plays, of Hanukkah games.

From the top bunk comes the start of a Hanukkah song:

Oh, you tiny candlelights
Stories you tell
Stories without end.

Slowly, softly, from all corners of the barrack, voices join in:

You tell of many bloody deeds
Of bravery and skill
Of wonders long ago.

Somehow strengthened, raising our voices higher, we all sing:

When I see you twinkling bright
A dream arises brilliantly
Speaks an old dream.
Jews, there were battles you waged
Jews, there were victories
All so hard to believe.

Suddenly the guard's pounding at the door brings us back to cruel reality. "What is going on? Be still!" she shouts, banging with her rifle at the door. "Stop, or I'll come in!"

We stop. A smile spreads over my face.
The emptiness is gone. I feel happy.

"We, too, have just won a victory,"
I whisper softly to the girl next to me.
Her hand touches mine. We press
hands silently.

MEET RUTH M. SENDER, AUTHOR

*Ruth Minsky Sender was born in Poland in 1926. She
spent her teenage years in a Nazi concentration camp and
wrote about her experiences in her first two books. She
states: "The Cage and To Life are my life story and the
story of the millions who perished during the Holocaust.
A million and a half children perished, their crime, they
were born Jewish. I am a Jew. I was a child during the
Holocaust, yet I survived. I feel, as one who did survive,
it is my duty to write, speak, and teach about it. I hope
the world will learn what hate, prejudice, and indifference
lead to. I feel I must tell of the human spirit that can still
hope when all is hopeless. 'As long as there is life there is
hope.' Those were my mother's words that helped me survive. I believe that we must never lose hope. Never give
up . . . Even as a child I always wanted to teach and
write. I wrote poems even in the Nazi death camps. They
helped me to hold on to hope, to life."*

ANNE FRANK:
THE DIARY OF A YOUNG GIRL
translated from the Dutch
by B. M. Mooyaart-Doubleday
illustrated by Susan Keeter

During World War II, many Jewish families in Germany and elsewhere in Europe hid to avoid being sent to concentration camps. Anne Frank and her family moved to Holland to escape the Nazis. When the Nazis came to Holland, the Franks hid for two years in a secret annex in Mr. Frank's office building. During this time, Anne kept a diary of her daily thoughts, feelings, and activities. Her father found these diaries after her death in a concentration camp in 1945 and had them published. These are a few of her first diary entries.

I hope I shall be able to confide in you completely,
as I have never been able to do in anyone before, and I hope that
you will be a great support and comfort to me.
Anne Frank, 12 June 1942.

Wednesday, 8 July, 1942

Dear Kitty,

Years seem to have passed between Sunday and now. So much has happened, it is just as if the whole world had turned upside down. But I am still alive, Kitty, and that is the main thing, Daddy says.

Yes, I'm still alive, indeed, but don't ask where or how. You wouldn't understand a word, so I will begin by telling you what happened on Sunday afternoon.

At three o'clock (Harry had just gone, but was coming back later) someone rang the front doorbell. I was lying lazily reading a book on the veranda in the sunshine, so I didn't hear it. A bit later, Margot appeared at the kitchen door looking very excited. "The S.S. have sent a call-up notice for Daddy," she whispered. "Mummy has gone to see Mr. Van Daan already." (Van Daan is a friend who works with Daddy in the business.) It was a great shock to me, a

call-up; everyone knows what that means. I picture concentration camps and lonely cells—should we allow him to
be doomed to this? "Of course he won't go," declared Margot, while we waited together. "Mummy has gone to the
Van Daans to discuss whether we should move into our
hiding place tomorrow. The Van Daans are going with us,
so we shall be seven in all." Silence. We couldn't talk any
more, thinking about Daddy, who, little knowing what was
going on, was visiting some old people in the Joodse
Invalide; waiting for Mummy, the heat and suspense, all
made us very overawed and silent.

Suddenly the bell rang again. "That is Harry," I said.
"Don't open the door." Margot held me back, but it was not
necessary as we heard Mummy and Mr. Van Daan downstairs, talking to Harry, then they came in and closed the
door behind them. Each time the bell went, Margot or I
had to creep softly down to see if it was Daddy, not opening
the door to anyone else.

Margot and I were sent out of the room. Van Daan wanted to talk to Mummy alone. When we were alone together
in our bedroom, Margot told me that the call-up was not for
Daddy, but for her. I was more frightened than ever and
began to cry. Margot is sixteen; would they really take girls
of that age away alone? But thank goodness she won't go,
Mummy said so herself; that must be what Daddy meant
when he talked about us going into hiding.

Into hiding—where would we go, in a town or the country, in a house or a cottage, when, how, where . . . ?

These were questions I was not allowed to ask, but I couldn't get them out of my mind. Margot and I began to pack some of our most vital belongings into a school satchel. The first thing I put in was this diary, then hair curlers, handkerchiefs, schoolbooks, a comb, old letters; I put in the craziest things with the idea that we were going into hiding. But I'm not sorry, memories mean more to me than dresses.

At five o'clock Daddy finally arrived, and we phoned Mr. Koophuis to ask if he could come around in the evening. Van Daan went and fetched Miep. Miep has been in the business with Daddy since 1933 and has become a close friend, likewise her brand-new husband, Henk. Miep came and took some shoes, dresses, coats, underwear, and stockings away in her bag, promising to return in the evening. Then silence fell on the house; not one of us felt like eating anything, it was still hot and everything was very strange. We let our large upstairs room to a certain Mr. Goudsmit, a divorced man in his thirties, who appeared to have nothing to do on this particular evening; we simply could not get rid of him without being rude; he hung about until ten o'clock. At eleven o'clock Miep and Henk Van Santen arrived. Once again, shoes, stockings, books, and underclothes disappeared into Miep's bag and Henk's deep pockets, and at eleven-thirty they too disappeared. I was dog-tired and although I knew that it would be my last night in my own bed, I fell asleep immediately and didn't wake up until Mummy called me at five-thirty the next morning. Luckily it was not so hot as Sunday; warm rain fell steadily all day. We put on heaps of clothes as if we were going to the North Pole, the sole reason being to take clothes with us. No Jew in our situation would have dreamed of going out with a suitcase full of clothing. I had on two vests, three pairs of pants, a dress, on top of that a skirt, jacket, summer coat, two pairs of stockings, lace-up shoes, woolly cap, scarf, and still more; I was nearly stifled before we started, but no one inquired about that.

Margot filled her satchel with schoolbooks, fetched her bicycle, and rode off behind Miep into the unknown, as far as I was concerned. You see I still didn't know where our secret hiding place was to be. At seven-thirty the door closed behind us. Moortje, my little cat, was the only creature to whom I said farewell. She would have a good home with the neighbors. This was all written in a letter addressed to Mr. Goudsmit.

There was one pound of meat in the kitchen for the cat, breakfast things lying on the table, stripped beds, all giving the impression that we had left helter-skelter. But we didn't care about impressions, we only wanted to get away, only escape and arrive safely, nothing else. Continued tomorrow.

Yours, Anne

Thursday, 9 July, 1942
Dear Kitty,
So we walked in the pouring rain, Daddy, Mummy, and I, each with a school satchel and shopping bag filled to the brim with all kinds of things thrown together anyhow.

We got sympathetic looks from people on their way to work. You could see by their faces how sorry they were they couldn't offer us a lift; the gaudy yellow star spoke for itself.

Only when we were on the road did Mummy and Daddy begin to tell me bits and pieces about the plan. For months as many of our goods and chattels and necessities of life as possible had been sent away and they were sufficiently ready for us to have gone into hiding of our own accord on July 16. The plan had had to be speeded up ten days because of the call-up, so our quarters would not be so well organized, but we had to make the best of it. The hiding place itself would be in the building where Daddy has his office. It will be hard for outsiders to understand, but I shall explain that later on. Daddy didn't have many people working for him: Mr. Kraler, Koophuis, Miep, and Elli Vossen, a twenty-three-year-old typist who all knew of our arrival. Mr. Vossen, Elli's father, and two boys worked in the warehouse; they had not been told.

A photo of the building in which
the Franks hid.

I will describe the building: there is a large warehouse on the ground floor which is used as a store. The front door to the house is next to the warehouse door, and inside the front door is a second doorway which leads to a staircase (A). There is another door at the top of the stairs, with a frosted glass window in it, which has "Office" written in black letters across it. That is the large main office, very big, very light, and very full. Elli, Miep, and Mr. Koophuis work there in the daytime. A small dark room containing the safe, a wardrobe, and a large cupboard leads to a small somewhat dark second office. Mr. Kraler and Mr. Van Daan used to sit here, now it is only Mr. Kraler. One can reach Kraler's office from the passage, but only via a glass door which can be opened from the inside, but not easily from the outside.

From Kraler's office a long passage goes past the coal store, up four steps and leads to the showroom of the whole building: the private office. Dark, dignified furniture, linoleum and carpets on the floor, radio, smart lamp, everything first-class. Next door there is a roomy kitchen with a hot-water faucet and a gas stove. Next door the W.C. [water closet]. That is the first floor.

A wooden staircase leads from the downstairs passage to the next floor (B). There is a small landing at the top. There is a door at each end of the landing, the left one leading to a storeroom at the front of the house and to the attics. One of those really steep Dutch staircases runs from the side to the other door opening on to the street (C).

The right-hand door leads to our "Secret Annexe." No one would ever guess that there would be so many rooms hidden behind that plain gray door. There's a little step in front of the door and then you are inside.

There is a steep staircase immediately opposite the entrance (E). On the left a tiny passage brings you into a room which was to become the Frank family's bed-sitting-room, next door a smaller room, study and bedroom for the two young ladies of the family. On the right a little room without windows containing the washbasin and a small W.C. compartment, with another door leading to Margot's and my room. If you go up the next flight of stairs and open the door, you are simply amazed that there could be such a big light room in such an old house by the canal. There is a gas stove in this room (thanks to the fact that it was used as a laboratory) and a sink. This is now the kitchen for the Van Daan couple, besides being general living room, dining room, and scullery.

A tiny little corridor room will become Peter Van Daan's apartment. Then, just as on the lower landing, there is a large attic. So there you are, I've introduced you to the whole of our beautiful "Secret Annexe."

Yours, Anne

Friday, 10 July, 1942
Dear Kitty,

I expect I have thoroughly bored you with my long-winded descriptions of our dwelling. But still I think you should know where we've landed.

But to continue my story—you see, I've not finished yet—when we arrived at the Prinsengracht, Miep took us quickly upstairs and into the "Secret Annexe." She closed

A photo of the attic where Anne did most of her writing.

the door behind us and we were alone. Margot was already waiting for us, having come much faster on her bicycle. Our living room and all the other rooms were chock-full of rubbish, indescribably so. All the cardboard boxes which had been sent to the office in the previous months lay piled on the floor and the beds. The little room was filled to the ceiling with bedclothes. We had to start clearing up immediately, if we wished to sleep in decent beds that night. Mummy and Margot were not in a fit state to take part; they were tired and lay down on their beds, they were miserable, and lots more besides. But the two "clearers-up" of the family—Daddy and myself—wanted to start at once.

The whole day long we unpacked boxes, filled cupboards, hammered and tidied, until we were dead beat. We sank into clean beds that night. We hadn't had a bit of anything warm the whole day, but we didn't care; Mummy and Margot were too tired and keyed up to eat, and Daddy and I were too busy.

On Tuesday morning we went on where we left off the day before. Elli and Miep collected our rations for us, Daddy improved the poor blackout, we scrubbed the kitchen floor, and were on the go the whole day long again. I hardly had time to think about the great change in my life until Wednesday. Then I had a chance, for the first time since our arrival, to tell you all about it, and at the same time to realize myself what had actually happened to me and what was still going to happen.

Yours, Anne

MUSIC AND SLAVERY

Wiley
illustrated by Ashley Bryan

The Banjo Lesson. 1893.
Henry O. Tanner.

Oil on canvas. Hampton
University Museum

Mother was let off some days at noon to get ready for spinning that evening. She had to portion out the cotton they was gonna spin and see that each got a fair share. When mother was going round counting the cards each had spun she would sing this song:

Keep your eye on the sun.
See how she run.
Don't let her catch you with your work undone.
I'm a trouble, I'm a trouble.
Trouble don't last always.

That made the women all speed up so they could finish before dark catch 'em, 'cause it be mighty hard handlin' that cotton thread by firelight.

BOB ELLIS
slave in Virginia

The life of many slaves in the United States was often full of fear and misery. Long hours were often spent picking cotton in the hot summer sun. At night, the slaves ate what little food their owners had given them and frequently slept on dirt floors. The slaves lived in run-down, overcrowded cabins and owned only the few clothes and possessions their masters had given them. They lived in fear of being beaten if they did not work hard enough or disobeyed their owners. They were not paid, and they were not allowed to leave their homes without special permission.

These terrible living conditions and lack of freedoms made many slaves want to escape. For most, however, there was no real hope of escape. Each day was a struggle to survive. One way the slaves dealt with these hardships was through music. It was a way to express both their sadness and their hope.

The slaves brought with them from Africa a strong tradition of music. Song and dance were an important part of their daily lives. They sang as they worked. They sang to celebrate. They sang when they were sad. They continued this tradition in the new world.

Slaves also brought instruments with them. The drum was the most important instrument used by them in Africa. However, many slave owners believed drums were being used to send secret messages. Therefore, drums were forbidden on most plantations. Instead, slaves kept the strong rhythms of their songs by clapping their hands, stomping their feet, swaying their bodies, and using other instruments such as the banjo. The banjo, developed by the slaves, became a commonly used instrument and is still in use today.

Many of the songs the slaves sang were developed as they worked in the fields. Singing helped take their minds off the difficulties of their work. These songs often changed over time. Many songs required a leader who would sing one line of the song while the others sang the response. These "call and response" chants were unique to slave music. Some songs that survived have become well-known spirituals, or religious songs. These songs, including "Swing Low Sweet Chariot" and "Go Down Moses," are based on stories in the Bible in which people were kept as slaves. Slaves were punished, often severely beaten, if they spoke against slavery. Through the spirituals, they could sing about the brutality of slavery without fear of being punished. Many of these songs are still sung today and are a tribute to the rich musical heritage of the slaves.

MANY THOUSAND GONE

No more auc-tion block for me,   No more,   No more,

No more auc-tion block for me,   Ma- ny thou-sand gone.

No more peck of corn for me,
No more,
No more,
No more peck of corn for me,
Many thousand gone.

No more hundred lash for me,
No more,
No more,
No more hundred lash for me,
Many thousand gone.

WALK TOGETHER CHILDREN

O, Walk to-geth-er child-ren, Don't you get wea-ry,
Sing to-geth-er child-ren, Don't you get wea-ry,

Walk to-geth-er child-ren, Don't you get wea-ry,
Sing to-geth-er child-ren, Don't you get wea-ry,

Walk   to- geth- er child- ren,   Don't you get wea- ry, There's a
Sing   to- geth- er child- ren,   Don't you get wea- ry, There's a

great camp meet- ing in the Prom- ised Land.

Going to mourn and ne- ver tire, — Mourn and ne- ver

tire, — Mourn and nev- er tire, — There's a

great camp meet - ing in the Prom- ised Land. O,

FINE ART
SURVIVING

Minamoto no Yorinobu swimming across a bay to attack the rebellious Tadatsune. 1879. Tsukioka Yoshitoshi.

Woodblock print. Robert Schaap Collection, Vincent van Gogh Museum, Rijksmuseum, Amsterdam. Photo: Asian Art and Archaeology/Art Resource

The Old Plantation. c. 1790–1800. Artist unknown.

Watercolor on laid paper. Abby Aldrich Rockefeller Folk Art Center. Photo: © Colonial Williamsburg Foundation

Voyagers in a Snowdrift on Mount Tarrar. 1829. Joseph Mallord William Turner.

Watercolor. British Museum, London

Buchenwald concentration camp survivors. 1945. Margaret Bourke-White.

Photograph. Estate of Margaret Bourke-White. Photo: © 1945 Time Warner Inc., *Life* magazine

Choctaw Removal. 1966. Valjean McCarty Hessing.

Watercolor. Philbrook Museum of Art, Tulsa, Oklahoma. Photo: Lassiter-Shoemaker Photography

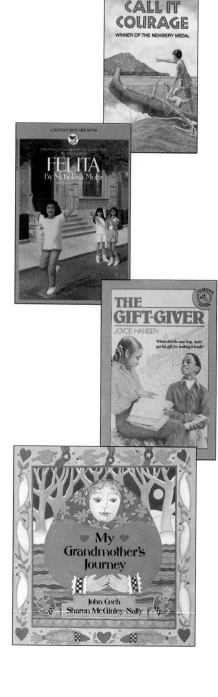

BIBLIOGRAPHY

Call It Courage by Armstrong Sperry. Facing the dangers of the sea, Mafatu learns about courage.

Felita by Nicholasa Mohr. Felita moves to a new neighborhood with shocking results.

The Gift-Giver by Joyce Hansen. Can Amir and Doris find hope in their inner-city neighborhood? Read about life on 163rd Street in the Bronx.

My Grandmother's Journey by John Cech. A grandmother embarks on an amazing trip around the world.

My Side of the Mountain by Jean Craighead George. Learning how to live off the land, a boy spends an exciting year alone in the Catskill mountains.

North American Indian Survival Skills by Karen Liptak. How did the Native Americans survive without modern technology? Read and find out their amazing secrets!

The Planet of Junior Brown by Virginia Hamilton. Two eighth-grade boys try to survive in an underground world.

You Can Survive by Howard E. Smith, Jr. Could you survive in the wilderness, alone? Would you be able to find food and shelter? These and other questions will be answered in this book.

TECHNOLOGY

THE WONDERS OF THE PYRAMIDS

Geraldine Woods
illustrated by Jan Adkins

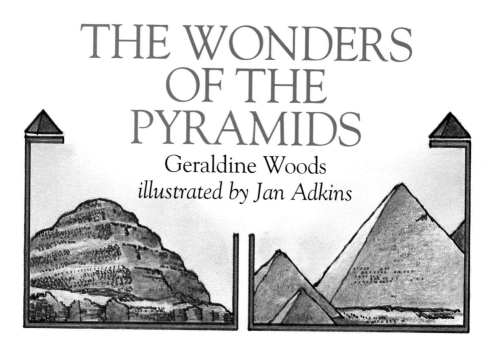

In a travel guide for ancient tourists, the Greek writer
Philon called the Great Pyramid at Giza one of the
wonders of the world. Scientists who have studied the
construction of the pyramids would agree—these monumental structures are indeed one of the most remarkable
achievements of ancient times.

Archeologists have identified the remains of over eighty
pyramids in Egypt, all tombs for pharaohs and other noble
Egyptians. The step pyramid built for King Djoser about
2680 B.C. is the oldest—and also the first large building
ever constructed entirely of stone. According to an
ancient Egyptian writing, the step design was meant to be
"a staircase to heaven . . . for [the pharaoh]." As Egyptian

builders became more skilled, they changed the steps into a true pyramid, the sacred sign for their sun god, Ra.

The Great Pyramid of the pharaoh Khufu (usually known by his Greek name, Cheops) is the largest. It covers 13 acres and contains 2,250,000 blocks of stone, averaging 5,000 pounds each. It's hard to imagine how anyone could construct such an enormous building, even today. Moreover, the Egyptians employed only three simple machines in building the pyramids—the lever, the inclined plane, and the wedge.

The first steps in construction were to clear the area of sand and gravel until the desert's rock floor was exposed and then to make the site perfectly level. Even a slight difference in height between one side of the pyramid and another could cause the entire structure to come crashing down.

How do you make sure that 13 acres of land are perfectly flat, without modern instruments? The Egyptians used water. They knew that free-flowing water always forms a level surface, so the Egyptians dug a network of trenches that crisscrossed the base area of the pyramid. They flooded the trenches, then marked the water line on the sides.

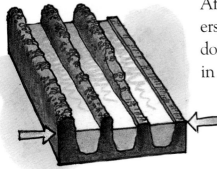

After draining the trenches, laborers cut the surface of the ground down to the watermarks and filled in the trenches with rubble.

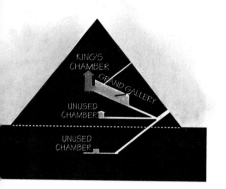

Meanwhile, architects were drawing the plan of the building on clay tablets. Although a pyramid appears to be a solid mass of stone, it actually contains a number of tunnels and rooms. There was a chamber for the pharaoh's sarcophagus (a stone coffin) and another for treasures the ruler would need in the next life. A passage from the outside was built for carrying the pharaoh's body to its resting place. In some pyramids, chambers for the pharaoh's wife were also included.

Many pyramids contained false tunnels and empty rooms to make things harder for tomb robbers. Unfortunately these chambers also created difficulties for the builders. The pyramids were constructed in layers. Once the thousands of blocks that made up each level were in place, it was almost impossible to move them. Therefore the builders had to be extremely careful to plan the proper position of openings.

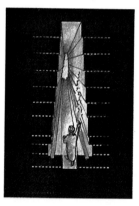

The pyramids were built around a core of limestone from the western desert, only a short distance from the building site. The interior chambers were usually made of granite, which was quarried at Aswan, about 500 miles upriver. The outer surfaces of the pyramids were covered with pure white limestone from across the Nile near Cairo in eastern Egypt. The architects listed the number, type, and measurements of the stones they needed. Scribes sent copies to the quarries, where work gangs filled the orders.

Before cutting stone, workers first drew marks on the rock to outline each block. Then, with chisels and mallets, they chipped a series of small cracks into the stone. Next, the workers hammered wooden wedges into the cracks and soaked the area with water. As the water was absorbed by the dry wood, the wedges swelled and split the rock.

The rough-cut blocks of stone then had to be transported to the building site. To raise each block, the workers probably tied ropes of palm fiber to it and tilted one side with a lever. Or the Egyptians may have used a weight arm to lift the blocks. A weight arm is made of heavy timber. It has a central post and two arms, one short and one long. A sling is slipped under the block and attached to the short arm. Small rocks are placed on a platform attached to the long arm until they almost balance the weight of the block. The block rises when the long arm is tipped.

Once the block was raised, a wooden sled was

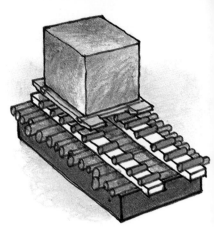

quickly slipped underneath. A team of men pulled the sled, following a path of logs that kept the sled from sinking into the sand. The blocks were brought to the Nile and loaded on barges, which carried them to the building site.

When they arrived, the blocks still had to be smoothed and cut to exact size. Workers cut away the larger bumps with saws or chisels and mallets. Then they rubbed the surface with rough stone or a lump of extremely hard rock called dolerite. The corners of each block were measured to be sure that they were perfectly square. The workers used wooden right angles and knocked away any extra rock with chisels or pieces of flint.

Many of the pyramids contained underground rooms. Before construction could begin, these chambers had to be excavated. To make the digging easier, the Egyptians probably worked with caissons. Caissons, which are still used in the construction of tunnels, are hollow cylinders made of stone and brick. The caisson is placed on the site, and the diggers work inside it. As the dirt is removed, the caisson is

pushed forward. Its strong walls keep the hole from caving in.

After the Egyptians dug the underground chambers, it was time to actually move the pyramid stones into position. The blocks were dragged into place on sleds or rollers made of logs. To carry blocks to the higher layers, huge ramps made of mud and sand were built on the sides of the pyramids. Workers probably sprinkled water or oil over the stones to make them slide more easily over one another. The blocks fitted together so well that no mortar was needed to hold them in place. In most places, the seam between blocks was so tight that not even the blade of a knife could be inserted. As each layer was finished, a surveyor checked that the edges were perfectly square and that the layer was rising at the correct angle.

When it was time to put a roof over an inner chamber, workers filled the room with dirt. They set the roof stones in place and then removed the dirt through the chamber's doorway. Stoneworkers finished the interior of the room, usually with granite.

The very top of the pyramid was the capstone, a perfectly pointed stone with a plug on its lower side. The plug fit into a hole on the preceding layer. Once the capstone was in place, stoneworkers began to polish the outside of the pyramid. As they traveled toward the base, workers removed the dirt ramps. When the last ramp was removed, the pyramid was finished—a path to heaven for the pharaoh, and a monument to the earthly labor of the Egyptians.

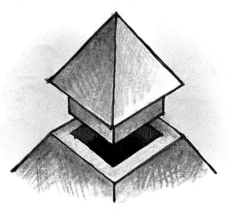

THE GREAT WALL OF CHINA
written and illustrated by
Leonard Everett Fisher

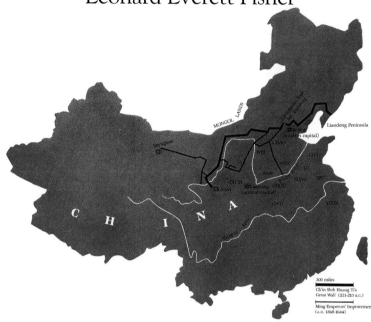

A bout twenty-two hundred years ago, King Cheng of Ch'in conquered the kingdoms of Han, Sung, Yen, Yüeh, Ch'i, Chou, Chao, Ch'u, Wei, Wey, Wu, and Lu. Tiny Ch'in became a huge empire: China. And King Cheng became Ch'in Shih Huang Ti, the First Supreme Emperor of China.

China was difficult to manage. Each of the old kingdoms had its own system of weights, measures, money, and writing. A grain of rice in Chao did not weigh the same in

Chou. A hat size in Han was not the same in Sung. Money earned in Ch'i could not be spent in Ch'u. And officials in Wu could not read reports from officials in Lu. But the emperor brought order to his unwieldy lands. He made the systems of weights, measures, money, and writing the same everywhere. He even made everyone wear the same color: black.

Bringing order to his empire was not Ch'in Shih Huang Ti's only problem. In the north, fierce Mongol horsemen raided Chinese villages. They attacked the people and stole their goods. The Mongols threatened to invade all of China.

The guards flung a man at the emperor's feet. His clothes were torn and caked with mud. He had run a long way with his news. He trembled with fear.

"O Mighty Sire," he cried, "the Mongols have destroyed many villages in Wei. My own village has been turned to ashes. I alone have escaped."

Ch'in Shih Huang Ti rose in anger. "I must stop these barbarians!" he roared at the royal advisors.

"They are cruel," warned Li Ssu, the Prime Minister.

"They are tricky," added Chao Kao, Minister of the Household.

"And they are strong," declared Grand General Meng Tian.

"Soon they will fall on us," wailed the emperor's oldest son and Keeper of the Seals. "What will become of us? How shall we save ourselves?"

"With a wall!" Ch'in Shih Huang Ti bellowed.

"A wall? What wall?" the royal advisors asked. "We have many walls. None of them can stop these barbarians."

"I shall fix the old walls," replied the emperor. "I shall build a new and mightier wall and shall join all the walls together. I shall have one long wall across the top of China. It will stretch from Liaodong in the east to Lintao in the west. It will be six horses wide at the top, eight at the bottom, and five men high. I shall build it at the edge of our steepest mountains. No Mongol barbarian will be able to go around it, over it, under it, or through it. It will be the Great Wall!"

Ch'in Shih Huang Ti ordered Grand General Meng Tian to make preparations. The general's soldiers grabbed criminals, cheats, troublemakers, and anyone the emperor did not like. They dragged humble people from their homes. They forced musicians, teachers, writers, and artists to join the army of workers.

"And take that whining son of mine, Fu Su," the emperor commanded.

When all was ready, Grand General Meng Tian mounted his horse. With a wave of his arm, seven hundred thousand workers and three hundred thousand soldiers—one million people—marched north to build Ch'in Shih Huang Ti's Great Wall.

Tens of thousands were put to work fixing the old walls. Thousands more were made to pound the earth into thick, high mounds and to shape the mounds with bamboo poles.

Mobs of workers made huge, heavy bricks from clay. They cut large, square stones as well. These they fitted to the sides and tops of the earthen mounds. The entire wall,

from one end of Ch'in Shih Huang Ti's China to the other, they faced with brick and stone.

Every one hundred yards, the workers built watchtowers two stories high. Now the Mongols could be seen coming. Warning signals could be sent. There would be no more surprise attacks.

The Mongols watched from distant hills. They were unable to attack so many workers and soldiers on the high slopes.

No one was allowed to rest.

"You, there!" screamed the soldiers, cracking their whips. "Faster! Faster! Work! Work! No idlers here!"

The Chinese worked day and night. Workers who complained or who ran away were caught and buried alive. Many workers lived out their lives building the wall. Many were buried in the wall.

The wall grew slowly, winding up and down the mountains. Roadways at the top were paved with three layers of brick. They connected the watchtowers. They were wide enough to hold ten soldiers side by side.

Finally, after ten years of labor, the wall was finished. Ch'in Shih Huang Ti came to inspect his Great Wall. He was overjoyed.

"I have stopped the Mongols," he shouted. "We are saved at last. Forever."

MEET LEONARD EVERETT FISHER, AUTHOR AND ILLUSTRATOR

Leonard Everett Fisher has illustrated over two hundred books, many of them historical. He decided to write a story about the Great Wall after visiting the People's Republic of China in 1984. He has also designed U.S. and foreign postage stamps. Fisher first considers himself a painter. He states: "I am a painter because there are things that cannot be said in any other way."

YOU NEVER CAN TELL

adapted and illustrated by Janice Holland
translated by Arthur W. Hummel

L ong ago in China, when all the land was fair and
green, there lived an old man and his wife.

Their life was simple, and above all else they
loved three things: their son, their horse, and their farm.

They loved their son for reasons that everyone knows.
They loved their horse because he was strong and pulled
their plow.

They loved their farm, for in its yellow earth grew all the food that gave them life.

The son was named Liang. The horse was named Chih-tu. But the farm was so small that it had no name at all.

One day, for reasons which no one knows, their horse wandered away.

The farmer and his son, Liang, looked by the white waters that foamed in the brook. But the horse, Chih-tu, was not there.

Together the farmer and his son searched the road to the Jade Pagoda. But their horse was nowhere to be seen.

Dusty and tired, they started for home.

By this time the farmer's wife had told all the neighbors that the horse, Chih-tu, was lost. So when the farmer and his son drew near the house, they heard a great sound of wailing and weeping, for every neighbor had also a horse which he loved, and the loss of one horse struck terror into the hearts of all.

The oldest man in the village stroked his beard. "Your horse has no doubt wandered beyond the Great Wall into no-man's-land," he croaked.

"The fierce horsemen who live there must have stolen him by now!" said the schoolmaster.

"Never again will you see that horse," said the maker of shoes. "Sorrow and sadness. Woe and weeping. Ill luck indeed has come to this house!" wailed all the neighbors together.

Now all this while the farmer stood by the door, listening and watching, but never saying a word.

"Come now," said the maker of shoes. "We are all here to join you in sorrow. But you do not seem sad. Is it possible that you do not mind losing your horse? Without your horse you cannot plow your farm. Without plowing your farm you cannot grow your food. Without any food you will certainly starve!"

But the old farmer only shook his head and said, "You never can tell. This may turn out to be a good thing after all. You never can tell," he said. "You never can tell."

Day after day the farmer searched the road to the Jade Pagoda.

Day after day his son looked through the woods beside the foaming brook.

But the horse, Chih-tu, was gone.

The mid-autumn festival came and went. One moon followed another across the sky.

The old farmer sighed to himself. "Alas for Chih-tu. Alas."

And after that he searched no more.

Now it was early in the year, and the willow trees were pale, pale green. One morning the old farmer awoke long before dawn.

Thrump-de-dump! Thrump-de-dump!

The farmer sat straight up in bed.

Thrump-de-dump! Thrump-de-dump! Louder and louder grew the noise.

Quickly the farmer jumped out of his bed.

Quickly he hurried through the courtyard to the gate in the wall.

Just beyond the gate he could dimly see something moving. "Chih-tu!" he called. "Chih-tu!" Soon a soft velvet nose was thrust through the gate.

Chih-tu had come home!

The old farmer opened the gate, and Chih-tu trotted in, for all the world as though he had never been away.

Before the old man could close the gate, a strange black horse had followed Chih-tu into the courtyard.

The farmer stared. The strange horse was the most beautiful horse he had ever seen.

"Now where in this world did you come from?" he asked, half under his breath.

But the strange horse, of course, answered never a word.

Now the farmer knew all his neighbors for miles around, and their horses as well. So he went at dawn to the highway, and asked of all passers-by where the fine steed might belong.

But no one knew.

It was just as though the black horse had dropped from the sky.

Before many hours had passed the farmer's wife again told all the villagers the news.

"Just to think," she cackled in her high-pitched voice, "today we have two horses, whereas yesterday we had none at all!"

Now the villagers, always eager for a good time, crowded once more into the farmer's house.

"Heaven has smiled on this house today!" they shouted all together. "Gladness and joy. Good fortune and blessings. Heaven has smiled on this house today!"

But the old farmer only stood by the door, listening and watching, but never saying a word.

"Come now," said the schoolmaster. "We are here to make merry. Can it be that you do not rejoice in your luck?"

But the old farmer only smiled and said, "How do we know that this is such a good thing after all? You never can tell," he said. "You never can tell."

Happy were the days that followed for the farmer and his family! The red Chih-tu and the strange black horse worked together to plow the little farm.

Soon the yellow earth was ready for the planting. Soon the farmer's wheat was green above the ground. So well did everything grow that the farmer's son, Liang, had plenty of time to do as he liked.

Day after day Liang mounted one horse or the other and rode around the farm.

Day after day Liang practiced one clever stunt or another until his riding was the envy of all the villagers. At last he became so daring that there was no risk he would not take.

As one might have expected, it was not long before he fell from his horse and broke a leg.

By this time it was late summer, and the wheat was ready for the harvesting.

"Ah, weeping and woe!" cried the neighbors when they heard of the fall. "How will the old man harvest his wheat without the help of his son?"

Once more they flocked into the farmer's courtyard to comfort him in his trouble.

"Sorrow and sadness. Weeping and woe! Ill luck indeed has come to this house!" wailed all the neighbors together.

Now all this while the farmer stood by the door, listening and watching, but never saying a word.

"Come now," said the oldest man in the village. "We are all here to join you in sorrow. But you do not seem sad. Is it possible you do not mind that your son has broken his leg?"

But the old farmer only smiled and shook his head. "You never can tell. This may turn out to be a good thing after all. You never can tell," he said. "You never can tell."

Strange to say, soon after this the fierce horsemen broke through the Great Wall.

Down they came, like thunder, across the farms and fields. "Ai-yah!" they shrieked. "Ai-yah!"

They rode into the villages and broke through the gates and doors.

Each strong young man they could find was seized and bound, for the wild tribes were hard pressed in a desert war. They needed men to help them fight.

So many wild riders there were that the strongest youth could not resist them. Nine out of ten young men were seized and bound.

Swiftly the riders had come, and swiftly they now departed. Slowly the dust settled back into the lanes and courtyards. Among many families, only the old farmer's was safe from harm.

Because the father was old, and the son was still lame, the wild tribes had passed them by.

The neighbors soon came to see the old farmer. Sad they were, for their grief was still fresh. As they looked at his son they remembered their own brave sons who were gone.

Then the oldest man in the village spoke: "Strange are the ways of fate. The wild tribes came in my youth. Many of us were carried away, but many at last returned. Some gathered riches before they came home. Some went to the cities and rose to great power.

"So, here today, we shall not weep, for we have seen that the sorrows sometimes bring their blessings. Nor yet can our hearts make merry, for we have seen that the joys many times bring their sorrows. As for which is the good, and which is the bad, you have spoken most truly, 'You never can tell.'"

"He has spoken most truly, most truly indeed," said all the neighbors together.

"For you never can tell," they said. "You never can tell."

"Yes," agreed the old farmer. "That one thing is true. You never can tell," he said. "You never can tell."

THE WORKHORSE
from ONCE UPON A HORSE
by Suzanne Jurmain

Odin, the king of the Norse gods,
uses his mighty eight-legged horse in battle.

Illustration by Krystyna Stasiak

Once upon a time, back in the days of myth and magic, the Norse gods lived in the beautiful city of Asgard. Now these gods loved fighting and feasting, but they hated hard work. They never fixed anything, and that was why the walls of Asgard were in ruins when the giant came.

He arrived one morning, riding on the back of an enormous stallion. After running a shrewd eye over the tumbledown ramparts, he went up to Allfather Odin, king of the gods, and said, "I'll fix that wall for you—if you'll give me the sun, the moon, and the goddess of love for my wages."

As soon as he heard this outrageous offer, Odin went white with rage. But before he could bawl out the insolent giant, Loki the Trickster whispered, "Wait, Odin. Be smart. Tell the giant you'll pay if he rebuilds the wall in six months' time. He'll never meet the deadline. You'll never have to keep the bargain, and part of the work will be done for free."

This seemed like good advice, so Odin said, "Very well, giant, we'll pay your price—if you finish the job exactly one-half year from today."

"That's impossible!" cried the giant. Then he paused, and a crafty smile flickered around the corners of his mouth. "But I'll give it a try—if you'll let my horse help."

Odin agreed, figuring the horse couldn't do much. And that was a big mistake.

The giant's horse worked just as hard as the giant. Each morning the stallion hauled enormous loads of stone up to the ramparts. Each afternoon the giant cemented the stones into place. Each week the wall rose higher and higher. And when the deadline was only three days away, the battlements were almost complete. If the giant finished, the gods would have to pay. A worried Odin ordered Loki to find some way out of the predicament.

And Loki did. He transformed himself into a pretty mare, pranced off into the forest, and began to flirt with the giant's hardworking stallion. Soon the big horse was so madly in love that he forgot about his job. Instead of hauling stones, he ran off to play with his lady friend—and he didn't come back.

Work came to a standstill. The hours ticked by, and when the deadline came, the city walls were incomplete. The giant raged, Loki laughed, and Odin smiled quietly. After all, he thought, the business had turned out rather well. Asgard's new wall was high and strong. The repair work had been done for free, and Odin had acquired a useful piece of information. In six short months this mighty god had learned that the horse could be a strong, efficient worker.

It took centuries for mortals to make the same discovery.

Oxen used for work during the Middle Ages.

During ancient times people thought the horse was a high-priced, inefficient laborer—and they were right. In those days the horse was expensive to buy and to feed. It couldn't pull a heavy load. And it couldn't work in the fields because constant contact with damp, muddy ground damaged its delicate hoofs. The ancients sensibly saved their fast, fragile, expensive horses for sport and war. And they used cheap, hardy oxen, donkeys, and water buffaloes to pull plows, turn machines, and haul heavy wagons. Horses were excused from most everyday chores until the Middle Ages.

After learning to use the horse collar, around A.D. 800, Europeans realized that horses were strong enough to pull enormous loads. They found that little metal plates nailed to the horse's feet protected the animal's hoofs from the damp. Finally they developed a way to grow large oat crops, which brought the cost of owning a horse way down. By the end of the Middle Ages Europeans had transformed the horse into a cheap, practical, popular work animal. And they were the only people on earth who'd done it. In Asia, North Africa, and the Near East, where horses were always scarce and expensive, donkeys, oxen, and water buffaloes kept right on doing the heavy work. But after the Middle Ages Europe started to run on horsepower.

Farmers were the first to benefit. In the 1300s they realized that a horse could plow a field faster than an ox, and from that moment until the beginning of the twentieth century horses were the most popular farmhands in Europe.

Year after year, in season after season, the farmer and his horse worked side by side. At six-thirty in the cold gray mornings of early spring, they were already hard at work, doing the plowing. Up and down the field they paced, back and forth, walking eleven miles each time they tilled an acre. Summertime brought the harvest. On hot August days farmers cut the grain and horses threshed it, stamping and tramping on the new-cut sheaves to separate the valuable kernels from the straw. In September farm horses carried grain to the mill and flour to market. In October it was time for winter plowing. And when winter came, the farmer and his horse fetched wood for the fire, hauled fodder to the cattle, and rested—just a little—before it was time to plow the fields again in spring.

For many years farm horses had three basic jobs: plowing, threshing, and hauling. But in the nineteenth century things changed. In 1831 an American named Cyrus McCormick invented a horse-powered reaping machine that cut wheat quickly. Other inventors followed his lead, and soon farmers were using horse-drawn mowers, cultivators, diggers, planters, reapers, and cotton pickers. Farm horses were busier than ever, and field work was done faster than ever before. In the 1700s a single man with a sickle could cut half an acre of wheat in one day. By the late 1890s a farmer equipped with a team of twenty horses and a machine called a combine could

Harvesting wheat in eastern Oregon around 1900 with the help of a combine powered by thirty-six horses.
Oregon State University Archives

Horses hauling ore in a sixteenth-century European mining camp.

reap, thresh, and bag all the wheat grown on seventy acres in the same amount of time. With the help of the new horse-powered machines European, American, and Australian farmers were able to work less, cultivate more land, and grow more crops.

The workhorse was the farmer's friend and the factory hand's partner. The ancient Greeks and Romans occasionally used old, worn-out horses to turn machinery that powered olive presses, grape presses, and grain mills. That was the first time horses worked in factories. It certainly wasn't the last. Between 1500 and 1800 European industry ran on wind power, water power, and animal power.

For years horses powered machines that churned butter, pressed cider, refined sugar, and made gunpowder. They worked in textile mills. They worked in dye factories. And in Europe's iron mills, factory horses helped process ore that mine horses helped scoop out of the earth.

What could workhorses do? Almost anything. These animals hauled the bricks that built the bridges, the houses, the castles, the cathedrals, and the shops. Horses dragged the sculptor's marble from the quarries. They harvested the timber. Some even helped to excavate canals. Farmhand, factory hand, miner, and builder, the horse was the most useful animal in Europe. And when Europeans brought horses to the New World, these hardworking animals changed the way Native Americans lived and helped colonists build a brand-new nation.

In the centuries before Columbus reached the New World, most of the Native Americans on the Great Plains were farmers. They lived in little villages, made pottery, and tended their crops. Sometimes they fished or hunted rabbits and deer. Huge herds of buffalo wandered across the prairie, too, but the Plains Indians seldom killed these big shaggy animals because it was hard to track the fast-moving herds on foot.

When Europeans brought the first horses to North America in the 1500s, they had no intention of sharing these valuable animals with their Native American neighbors. Soon after arriving, Spanish settlers established laws making it a crime for a Native American to own or ride a horse. But these edicts could not be enforced. As soon as the Plains Indians realized that horses were useful, they stole animals from the settlers' corrals, rounded up strays, and started their own herds. By the 1600s Native American tribes on the Great Plains had already begun to master the art of horsemanship. In the 1700s they found that a mounted hunter could easily keep pace with a buffalo herd, and that discovery changed their lives. At the beginning of the eighteenth century many Plains tribes stopped planting crops. They left their quiet villages and became wandering

The use of horses made it easier for the Plains
Indians to hunt the buffalo.

Art Resource

hunters who lived on buffalo meat, dressed in buffalo skins, slept in buffalo-hide tents, and followed the buffalo herds across the prairies. To survive, this new kind of Plains Indian had to kill buffalo, and to do it, he needed a horse.

One century later thousands of hardy cow ponies helped U.S. citizens found a very different kind of business: the cattle industry. At the end of the Civil War most of the western United States was nothing but wide open spaces. There were few towns and few people, and the grasslands stretched for miles in every direction. It was great cow country, and in the 1860s settlers started using it to raise large herds of longhorn cattle.

In the early days ranchers didn't bother to build fences; they let their herds run loose. Millions of cattle roamed freely across the open range, and only the brand on its side

A cowboy and his horse try to head off a stampede.
The Bettmann Archive

distinguished one animal from another. If a rancher wanted to count or sell his cows, he had to catch them. And
cow catching was a job for experienced cowboys and cow
ponies.

Despite the name, cow ponies weren't ponies at all. They
were smart, tough, dependable full-sized horses. Born and

raised on the open range, these animals were broken for riding when they were four or five years old and worked with cows until they were ten or eleven. No one knew more about cattle than an experienced cow pony. A good one could find a missing cow on a dark night or stop a stampede all by itself. Cowboys were supposed to tell their horses what to do, but many a young ranch hand actually got his first lessons in cattle handling from a wise old horse.

On a ranch, horses usually worked hardest at certain times of the year. In early spring they helped bring in the newborn calves for branding. Later, in the autumn, men and horses on each ranch rounded up hundreds of full-grown cows that were ready for market and drove these enormous herds from Texas to the nearest railway stations in Abilene and Dodge City, Kansas, several hundred miles away.

It was a hard, dangerous trip. Rustlers, wolves, and bobcats all lurked beside the trails waiting to attack. Water was sometimes scarce, and grass was often in short supply. The cows could be slow, stubborn, wild, or just plain mean. Keeping track of these ornery creatures was a full-time job, and during a drive cowboys were always on the move, darting up and down the long line to speed up the slowpokes, slow down the speedsters, and push wanderers back into place.

Since no cow pony could stand more than half a day at a time of this grueling work, a cowboy usually took a string of six horses with him on the drive. He used two for morning work, two for afternoons, and since there were always

A roundup on a Kansas ranch, about 1900.

plenty of nighttime emergencies, he kept the best two for riding after dark.

The work was hard, but the job was important. Between the 1860s and the 1880s cowboys and cow ponies guided millions of cattle along the great western trails. They helped raise enough beef to feed a nation, and they turned the western states into a great "cattle kingdom."

The United States was a big country. By the time the Civil War broke out, it was one full continent wide and half a continent long. For years dreamers had talked about building a railroad that would link the West Coast with the distant East. The government put up money for the project, and in 1863 agents from two companies broke ground for America's first transcontinental railroad. In Sacramento, California, men hired by the Central Pacific Railroad soon started to lay track that headed east. In 1865, outside Omaha, Nebraska, employees of the Union Pacific Railroad picked up their tools and began working their way west.

In order to get the job done, these companies needed horsepower. During construction twenty-five thousand horses and mules worked for the Union Pacific, and the best of all these animal laborers was a spunky cart horse named Blind Tom.

Tom went to work for the railroad in the spring of 1866 and soon became the most popular employee in the outfit. Day after day he hauled supplies to the track-laying crew, and in twenty-seven months this horse carried 110,000 tons

Blind Tom hauling a rail flatcar near Cozad, Nebraska, in October 1866. The picture was taken by John Carbutt, a photographer hired to record the progress of Union Pacific construction.

Union Pacific Railroad

of rails, helped lay about a thousand miles of track, and became a hero to the hardworking railroad men.

On May 10, 1869, the long job finally ended. At a spot near Promontory, Utah, workers laid tracks that joined the two railroads, and a crowd watched Central Pacific president Leland Stanford drive in one last railway spike made of gold. Animals usually aren't invited to ceremonies like this, but one was present that day. Standing behind the proud workers, the curious reporters, and the pompous dignitaries was Blind Tom, the workhorse who'd done more than most men to build America's first transcontinental railroad.

Tom was one of the most famous workhorses and one of the last. By the time he started working for the Union Pacific, the great age of animal power was already coming to an end. In 1769 James Watt had invented the steam engine. By 1860 a Frenchman had built the first practical gasoline engine, and in 1892 a German inventor patented the first diesel. Since each of these machines could do the work of many animals, there was less demand for the muscle power a horse could provide. In the 1800s factories started to run on steam power. Between 1930 and 1950 most European, American, and Australian farmers traded their draft animals for tractors. Miners also learned to use machines, and each year fewer horses were needed underground. In 1913 seventy thousand ponies worked in English coalpits. Sixty-five years later the number had shrunk to about two hundred. And by 1988 there were only

This photograph, taken in the 1980s, shows one of the last pit
ponies to work in British mines.

British Coal Company

forty-three ponies left. At Ellington Colliery in the north of
England twenty-five of these animals still haul supplies to
miners working three hundred feet beneath the North Sea
floor. But even that arrangement may not last much longer,
for when these last pit ponies retire, authorities will probably
buy machines to take their place.

In mining—and every other industry—the age of the
workhorse has ended. Most of the jobs are gone. But the
word *horsepower*—which is still used to describe the amount
of work a machine can do—remains: one last relic of a time
when horses were the greatest workers in the Western world.

THE WONDERFUL MACHINE

from LITTLE HOUSE IN THE BIG WOODS
by Laura Ingalls Wilder
illustrated by Garth Williams

Autumn was great fun. There was so much work to do, so many good things to eat, so many new things to see. Laura was scampering and chattering like the squirrels, from morning to night.

One frosty morning, a machine came up the road. Four horses were pulling it, and two men were on it. The horses hauled it up into the field where Pa and Uncle Henry and Grandpa and Mr. Peterson had stacked their wheat.

Two more men drove after it another, smaller machine.

Pa called to Ma that the threshers had come; then he hurried out to the field with his team. Laura and Mary asked Ma, and then they ran out to the field after him. They might watch, if they were careful not to get in the way.

Uncle Henry came riding up and tied his horse to a tree. Then he and Pa hitched all the other horses, eight of them, to the smaller machine. They hitched each team to the end of a long stick that came out from the center of the machine. A long iron rod lay along the ground, from this machine to the big machine.

Afterward Laura and Mary asked questions, and Pa told them that the big machine was called the separator, and the rod was called the tumbling rod, and the little machine was called the horsepower. Eight horses were hitched to it and made it go, so this was an eight-horsepower machine.

A man sat on top of the horsepower, and when everything was ready he clucked to the horses, and they began to go. They walked around him in a circle, each team pulling on the long stick to which it was hitched, and following the team ahead. As they went around, they stepped carefully over the tumbling rod, which was tumbling over and over on the ground.

Their pulling made the tumbling rod keep rolling over, and the rod moved the machinery of the separator, which stood beside the stack of wheat.

All this machinery made an enormous racket, rackety-banging and clanging. Laura and Mary held tight to each other's hand, at the edge of the field, and watched with all their eyes. They had never seen a machine before. They had never heard such a racket.

Pa and Uncle Henry, on top of the wheat stack, were pitching bundles down on to a board. A man stood at the

board and cut the bands on the bundles and crowded the bundles one at a time into a hole at the end of the separator.

The hole looked like the separator's mouth, and it had long, iron teeth. The teeth were chewing. They chewed the bundles and the separator swallowed them. Straw blew out at the separator's other end, and wheat poured out of its side.

Two men were working fast, trampling the straw and building it into a stack. One man was working fast, sacking the pouring grain. The grains of wheat poured out of the separator into a half-bushel measure, and as fast as the measure filled, the man slipped an empty one into its place and emptied the full one into a sack. He had just time to empty it and slip it back under the spout before the other measure ran over.

All the men were working as fast as they possibly could, but the machine kept right up with them. Laura and Mary

were so excited they could hardly breathe. They held hands tightly and stared.

The horses walked around and around. The man who was driving them cracked his whip and shouted, "Giddap there, John! No use trying to shirk!" Crack! went the whip. "Careful there, Billy! Easy, boy! You can't go but so fast nohow."

The separator swallowed the bundles, the golden straw blew out in a golden cloud, the wheat streamed golden-brown out of the spout, while the men hurried. Pa and Uncle Henry pitched bundles down as fast as they could. And chaff and dust blew over everything.

Laura and Mary watched as long as they could. Then they ran back to the house to help Ma get dinner for all those men.

A big kettle of cabbage and meat was boiling on the stove; a big pan of beans and a johnny-cake were baking in the oven. Laura and Mary set the table for the threshers. They put on salt-rising bread and butter, bowls of stewed pumpkin, pumpkin pies and dried berry pies and cookies, cheese and honey and pitchers of milk.

Then Ma put on the boiled potatoes and cabbage and meat, the baked beans, the hot johnny-cake and the baked Hubbard squash, and she poured the tea.

Laura always wondered why bread made of corn meal was called johnny-cake. It wasn't cake. Ma didn't know, unless the Northern soldiers called it johnny-cake because the people in the South, where they fought, ate so much of it. They called the Southern soldiers Johnny Rebs. Maybe, they called the Southern bread, cake, just for fun.

Ma had heard some say it should be called journey-cake. She didn't know. It wouldn't be very good bread to take on a journey.

At noon the threshers came in to the table loaded with food. But there was none too much, for threshers work hard and get very hungry.

By the middle of the afternoon the machines had finished all the threshing, and the men who owned them drove them away into the Big Woods, taking with them the sacks of wheat that were their pay. They were going to the next place where neighbors had stacked their wheat and wanted the machines to thresh it.

Pa was very tired that night, but he was happy. He said to Ma:

"It would have taken Henry and Peterson and Pa and me a couple of weeks apiece to thresh as much grain with flails as that machine threshed today. We wouldn't have got as much wheat, either, and it wouldn't have been as clean.

"That machine's a great invention!" he said. "Other folks can stick to old-fashioned ways if they want to, but I'm all for progress. It's a great age we're living in. As long as I raise wheat, I'm going to have a machine come and thresh it, if there's one anywhere in the neighborhood."

He was too tired that night to talk to Laura, but Laura was proud of him. It was Pa who had got the other men to stack their wheat together and send for the threshing machine, and it was a wonderful machine. Everybody was glad it had come.

MEET GARTH WILLIAMS, ILLUSTRATOR
*When asked to illustrate a new version of the
Laura Ingalls Wilder books in 1944, Garth Williams was pleased.
"I loved and admired the books myself and they meant a great deal
to my small daughters when we read them aloud together. But my
knowledge of the West at that time was zero and I could not see
myself undertaking the work happily until I had seen the country
that formed the background of the stories. And so I decided to visit
Mr. and Mrs. Wilder in Mansfield, Missouri, and then follow the
route which the Ingalls family took in their covered wagon."
Williams tried to capture the people and settings in the stories as
Laura may have seen them.*

THRASHIN' TIME
written and illustrated by
David Weitzman

P a says the engine has the strength of sixty-five horses and the smoke from the stack can be seen for miles around. He says the engine gets the separator going so fast that the four of us will be doing all we can do just to keep up with it. That it will thrash more wheat in a day than you could imagine. "You'll have to be fast on the handle to feed one of those."

I saw a steam engine thrashin' wheat once, last year. Pa and Ma and Anna, my little sister, and I were out in the field piling the sheaves up in shocks, when I happened to look up. "Hey, look over west." Puffs of black smoke dusted the sky. Ma dropped the bundle she was stacking. "Oh, Gabe, it's a prairie fire!" Pa shielded his eyes against the noon sun and squinted at the smoke. "Naw, that's no fire, Maggie. See how the smoke's a-jumpin' up in the air like

that? Looks to me like they've one of those new steam engines workin' over at the Solheims'." Steam engine! I couldn't imagine such a thing on a farm.

Anna and I began pestering Pa to take us over to see the new engine. But it didn't take much doing. I could tell he wanted to go as much as we did. Pa glanced again at the smoke billowing into the sky. "Ya, sure, we can go. I'll finish up a bit here. Peter, you go hitch the horses up to the wagon. Maggie, if you and Anna put up a picnic, we'll go have us a look at that steam engine."

We got there to find that a lot of folks had come in wagons and buggies to gather 'round and watch the thrashin'. Steam engines were still new in these parts. And there it was, the engine with its dark blue boiler, shiny brass whistle, red wheels all decorated with yellow stripes, gears spinning and rods going back and forth, rocking gently in time to the puffs of smoke from the stack—*tucka-tucka-tucka-tucka-tucka*. The sounds, that's what I liked. *Tucka-tucka-tucka-tucka* and the little steam engine going *ss—ss—ss—ss—ss—ss—ss*. The engine was quieter than I thought it would be. It was almost alive like the horses working everywhere 'round it. And the horses. Why, I'll betcha there were sixty head, big horses—Belgians and Percherons —coming and going that afternoon. Teams pulled bundle wagons heaped tall with sheaves of wheat in from the fields, pulled wagons of yellow grain away from the separator to the silo. Another team hauled the water wagon, and another wagon brought loads of cord wood to keep the engine running sunup to sundown.

It was like the Fourth of July. Kids clambered up and slid down the hay stacks, played tag and skip-to-my-lou. Some of the men were pitching horseshoes and you could hear the thump of shoes fallen too short and the solid clank of a ringer. The women looked after all the little kids and put out lunches on big tables—heaps of potato salad, sandwiches, cakes and cookies and frosty pitchers of iced tea. Dogs napped in the dark cool under the wagons, not paying any mind to the puppies tumbling all over them. The older boys stood around together, pretending they were chewing plugs of tobacco, hawking and spitting, like the thrasher-men, only theirs wouldn't come brown. The men stood around the engine and the separator, puffing on their pipes, thumbs hooked under their suspenders. They inspected every part of that machine, pointing to this and that, looked up and down the belt stretching between the engine and separator in a long figure eight. Most of them had never seen a steam traction engine before.

Some of the older folks didn't like the new machine. "The old ways is the best ways," one of them said, tugging on his whiskers. "All this talk about steam engines is just a bunch of gibble-gabble," agreed another, "I'll stick to my oxen and horses." Others told of hearing all about engines exploding, killing and maiming the thrashin' crews, of careless engineers starting fires that burned up the farmer's whole crop and his barn besides. "Horses live off the land," Mr. Bauer said, "and don't need wood nor coal. No, nothin' but some hay and oats and we don't have to buy that! What's more they give you foals." He reached over and rubbed his hand down the neck of a stout gray Percheron mare hitched to a grain wagon. "All you get from steam engines is debt." Mr. Bjork agreed, "and what would we do for fertilizer? Steam engines don't make much manure, you know." Everyone laughed. "More trouble than they're worth. Why, last year Silas McGregor had to come borrow my oxen to pull his engine out of the mud. Wouldn't have one of those smoke-snortin' strawburners on my place," old Mr. Erstad scoffed, turning and waving away the scene.

But Mr. Torgrimson, now I could tell he was enjoying it. We were looking at the steam engine there up on the boiler, the connecting rod whizzing back and forth and the flywheel spinning so that the spokes were just a red blur. He was smiling and his eyes just twinkled. Then he pointed the stem of his pipe at the engine, squinted in a thoughtful way and rocked back and forth on his heels. "You know, Peter, that's a wonderful thing, the steam engine. You're witnessin' the beginnin's of real scientific farmin'." He couldn't take his eyes off that engine. "I read about a steam outfit—over Casselton way it was—that thrashed more than six thousand bushels in one day! Imagine that, six thousand bushels in just one day! Why you and your Ma and Pa all workin' together couldn't do more'n twenty or thirty in the same time."

Mr. Torgrimson was the one who told me about bonanza farming, where a bunch of engines would start out together, side-by-side, before daybreak, each pulling a fourteen-bottom plow almost as wide as our house. "They go all day, Peter, breakin' up thousands of acres of prairie grasslands before they rest at night—some even have head lamps so they can just keep going all night. The holdin's are so big, young fellow, that they go on 'n on for days like that 'fore they reach their line and turn 'round and plow back to where they started. Day after day, week after week they go up and back. Then they sowed all that land to wheat and thrashed one hundred and sixty-two thousand—here, I'll just write that number in the dust so you can see how big it is—162,000 bushels of wheat that season."

I could tell Pa liked the engine too. He got up on the wagon and pitched bundles for a while, and then stood on the engine platform talking to the engineer, Mr. Parker.

When he got down, he came over and put his hand on my shoulder, all the time looking at that engine, shaking his head like he couldn't believe his eyes. "Parker's got some machine there, by jippers, quite an outfit. What do you think about all this, Peter, steam power instead of horse power?"

I wasn't sure. "If the engine took the place of the horses, I think I'd miss Annie and Lulu and Quinn. Wouldn't you, Pa?"

"I would, but, you know, horse-power thrashin' is awful hard on them, son. Sure, I'd miss them, but we work them hard all year plowin', and diskin', and seedin' and mowin'. Then just when they're so tuckered out, about to drop and needin' a good rest, we put them to thrashin'. You and I both have seen too many good horses broken, seen them drop, die of the heat and tiredness right there in the traces. And for all their work we might get a hundred bushels, maybe two in a day. I don't know, Peter, maybe steam power is a better thing. I just don't know." Pa chuckled and his eyes got all crinkled and wrinkled with laugh lines the way they do. "I do know one thing though. If you asked the horses, I betcha they wouldn't be against this new steam power the way some folks 'round here are."

THRASHING DAY

Thrashing day begins when the engine is driven to the wheat field.

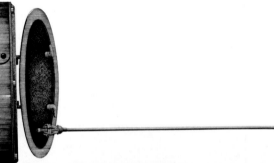

The engine's owner carefully checks the firebox to make sure everything is ready. Plenty of wood is needed for the fire.

The thrashers fling the wheat onto the feeder. The wheat is pulled inside the machine. There, it is beaten by the machine's metal teeth. As the wheat travels along the shaking rack inside, the grain separates from the straw. The straw is blown out the wind stack forty feet into the air. Meanwhile, the grain spills into the waiting wagon.

The thrashers must first connect the engine and the separator
with a long belt. The separator is the machine that separates the
wheat grain from the straw.

The water wagon driver, or tankee, must
keep enough water in the engine so that it
doesn't overheat and blow up.

When the work is done, the grain
wagon is driven to the elevator. The
grain is placed in bags to be sold and
later made into flour for bread.

GOING FOR THE DOCTOR

from BLACK BEAUTY by Anna Sewell
illustrated by Bill Farnsworth

*The following episode has been taken from the
autobiography of Black Beauty, a horse who lived in England
during the nineteenth century. Black Beauty had several
owners during his lifetime. Some were very cruel to him,
working him long hours. Others treated him as a favored
pet. In this episode, Black Beauty is being taken care of by
John and a new, young stableboy named Joe.*

One night, a few days after James had left, I had
eaten my hay and was laid down in my straw fast
asleep, when I was suddenly awoke by the stable
bell ringing very loud. I heard the door of John's house
open, and his feet running up to the Hall. He was back

again in no time; he unlocked the stable door, and came in, calling out, "Wake up, Beauty, you must go well now, if ever you did," and almost before I could think, he had got the saddle on my back and the bridle on my head; he just ran round for his coat, and then took me at a quick trot up to the Hall door. The Squire stood there with a lamp in his hand.

"Now, John," he said, "ride for your life, that is, for your mistress's life; there is not a moment to lose; give this note to Doctor White; give your horse a rest at the Inn, and be back as soon as you can."

John said "Yes, sir," and was on my back in a minute. The gardener who lived at the lodge had heard the bell ring, and was ready with the gate open, and away we went through the Park and through the village and down the hill till we came to the toll-gate. John called very loud and thumped upon the door: the man was soon out and flung open the gate.

"Now," said John, "do you keep the gate open for the Doctor; here's the money," and off we went again.

There was before us a long piece of level road by the river side; John said to me, "Now Beauty, do your best," and so I did; I wanted no whip nor spur, and for two miles I galloped as fast as I could lay my feet to the ground; I don't believe that my old grandfather who won the race at Newmarket could have gone faster. When we came to the bridge, John pulled me up a little and patted my neck. "Well done, Beauty! good old fellow," he said. He would have let me go slower, but my spirit was up, and I was off again as fast as before. The air was frosty, the moon was bright, it was very pleasant; we came through a village then through a dark wood, then uphill, then downhill, till after an eight miles' run we came to the town, through the streets and into the Market Place. It was all quite still except the clatter of my feet on the stones—everybody was asleep. The church clock struck three as we drew up at Doctor White's door. John rang the bell twice, and then knocked at the door like thunder. A window was thrown up, and Doctor White, in his nightcap, put his head out and said, "What do you want?"

"Mrs. Gordon is very ill, sir; master wants you to go at once, he thinks she will die if you cannot get there—here is a note."

"Wait," he said, "I will come."

He shut the window, and was soon at the door.

"The worst of it is," he said, "that my horse has been out all day and is quite done up; my son has just been sent for, and he has taken the other. What is to be done? Can I have your horse?"

"He has come at a gallop nearly all the way, sir, and I was to give him a rest here; but I think my master would not be against it if you think fit, sir."

"All right," he said, "I will soon be ready."

John stood by me and stroked my neck; I was very hot. The Doctor came out with his riding whip.

"You need not take that, sir," said John. "Black Beauty will go till he drops; take care of him, sir, if you can, I should not like any harm to come to him."

"No! no! John," said the Doctor, "I hope not," and in a minute we had left John far behind.

I will not tell about our way back; the Doctor was a heavier man than John, and not so good a rider; however, I did my very best. The man at the toll-gate had it open. When we came to the hill, the Doctor drew me up. "Now, my good fellow," he said, "take some breath." I was glad he did, for I was nearly spent, but that breathing helped me on, and soon we were in the Park. Joe was at the lodge gate, my master was at the Hall door, for he had heard us coming. He spoke not a word; the Doctor went into the house with him, and Joe led me to the stable. I was glad to get home, my legs shook under me, and I could only stand and pant. I had not a dry hair on my body, the water ran down my legs, and I steamed all over—Joe used to say, like a pot on the fire. Poor Joe! he was young and small, and as

yet he knew very little, and his father, who would have helped him, had been sent to the next village; but I am sure he did the very best he knew. He rubbed my legs and my chest, but he did not put my warm cloth on me; he thought I was so hot I should not like it. Then he gave me a pail full of water to drink; it was cold and very good, and I drank it all; then he gave me some hay and some corn, and thinking he had done right, he went away. Soon I began to shake and tremble, and turned deadly cold, my legs ached, my

loins ached, and my chest ached, and I felt sore all over. Oh! how I wished for my warm thick cloth as I stood and trembled. I wished for John, but he had eight miles to walk, so I lay down in my straw and tried to go to sleep. After a long while I heard John at the door; I gave a low moan, for I was in great pain. He was at my side in a moment stooping down by me; I could not tell him how I felt; but he seemed to know it all; he covered me up with two or three warm cloths, and then ran to the house for some hot water; he made me some warm gruel which I drank, and then I think I went to sleep.

John seemed to be very much put out. I heard him say to himself, over and over again, "Stupid boy! stupid boy! no cloth put on, and I dare say the water was cold too; boys are no good," but Joe was a good boy after all.

I was now very ill; a strong inflammation had attacked my lungs, and I could not draw my breath without pain.

John nursed me night and day, he would get up two or three times in the night to come to me; my master, too, often came to see me.

"My poor Beauty," he said one day, "my good horse, you saved your mistress's life, Beauty! yes, you saved her life." I was very glad to hear that, for it seems the Doctor had said if we had been a little longer it would have been too late. John told my master he never saw a horse go so fast in his life, it seemed as if the horse knew what was the matter. Of course I did, though John thought not; at least I knew as much as this, that John and I must go at the top of our speed, and that it was for the sake of the mistress.

MEET ANNA SEWELL, AUTHOR

Anna Sewell was born in Norfolk, England, in 1820. Shortly after her birth, her parents moved to London, where little Anna soon became fascinated by the horses used in those days to pull taxicabs. At age two, Anna insisted on being taken daily to a local cabstand to feed the horses. Anna spent her childhood holidays with relatives on a farm near London. There, her passion for horses grew as she learned to ride her aunt's pony and drive her uncle's carriage horses.

Years later, a conversation with a cab driver in London prompted Anna to write Black Beauty, *her only book. She was shocked to find out how badly her old friends the cab horses were treated, and she hoped her book would bring attention to the problems. Anna wrote* Black Beauty *from her bed during a seven-year illness, sometimes dictating chapters to her mother. Three months after the book was published, Anna died.*

The story is particularly interesting and admired because it is not only a story about a horse but a story told from the horse's point of view.

THE MESSENGER

from ONCE UPON A HORSE
by Suzanne Jurmain

At 10 P.M. on the night of April 18, 1775, Paul Revere hastily pulled on a pair of riding boots, said goodbye to his frightened wife, and quietly left his Boston house. His business was urgent. American spies had learned that British troops planned to seize rebel colonial leaders and weapons hidden in the nearby towns of Concord and Lexington on the following morning. Someone had to warn the townsfolk, and Paul Revere had volunteered to help spread the alarm.

When darkness came, each messenger mounted a fast horse, galloped through the silent, moonlit countryside, and roused the sleepy Massachusetts citizens with the cry, "The regulars are out! The British are coming!"

Frightened colonists tumbled from their beds and grabbed their muskets. When the British redcoats marched into Concord and Lexington on April 19, armed American patriots were waiting for them. Shots were fired, blood was shed, and that day marked the beginning of the American Revolution.

On that night in 1775 the swift horses ridden by Paul Revere and his companions carried a message that changed

A Minuteman and his horse deliver their message.

history. It was an important moment, but it wasn't unique. By the time Paul Revere jumped into the saddle that chilly April night, messengers on horseback had already carried thousands of dispatches that altered the fates of individuals and nations.

Today no one knows exactly who sent the first message by horse, but it might have been Cyrus the Great, a Persian king who established the world's first postal system twenty-four hundred years ago. Contemporaries called Cyrus "King of the World" because his immense empire stretched from the western edge of India, across Persia, to the shores of the Aegean Sea. To govern this vast realm, Cyrus needed a quick, efficient messenger service that could carry information to the capital and orders to the provinces.

Since that kind of regular mail service didn't exist when Cyrus mounted the throne, the King of the World invented one. He built relay stations along the main roads, hired men, bought a lot of fast horses, and put his service into operation. Whenever Cyrus or one of his ministers wanted to send a message, a courier picked up the dispatch, mounted a horse, and rode fifteen miles to the nearest relay station. There he stopped, changed horses, and rode on to the next relay point. When one rider tired, another took his place, and the message was passed from horseman to horseman until it reached its destination.

Persian couriers traveled at all hours and rode in all kinds of weather. They could carry a letter 180 miles in a single day, and their efficiency so impressed the ancient Greek traveler Herodotus that he wrote, "Neither snow nor rain nor heat nor gloom of night stays these couriers from swift completion of their appointed rounds." No one ever described the mail carrier's duty better, and today the words Herodotus wrote more than two thousand years ago are inscribed across the facade of the U.S. General Post Office in New York City.

The Persian system worked so well that other nations copied it. Several centuries after Cyrus's death the ancient

The metal "sole" of a
hipposandal.
© Erich Lessing/Art Resource

A carved stone relief shows an ancient
Roman postman driving his team.
© Erich Lessing/Art Resource

Romans—who had an even bigger empire to govern—
started a horse-powered postal service of their own.

Roman roads paved with huge stone blocks stretched
from Britain all the way to India. Hundreds of relay stations
lined these highways, and government couriers on horseback or in little horse-drawn wagons raced from station to
station. Since each courier's dispatch bag was packed with
secret messages, military reports, tax statements, and other
important state documents, Roman officials insisted on
prompt deliveries. Speed was essential, but constant galloping over long stretches of hard road in the damp European
climate damaged the horses' hoofs. To protect the feet of
these valuable animals, the Romans used an early type of
horseshoe called a hipposandal. This piece of footgear

looked like a lace-up shoe with a metal sole. It was clumsy, ugly, and hard to use, but it did the job. Hipposandals helped keep Roman post-horses on the road, and the messages those horses carried helped keep the Roman Empire running.

By the Middle Ages post-horses were carrying letters for the Arab sultans who ruled North Africa and the Near East. In Asia Genghis Khan's successors set up an elaborate mail system that was served by ten thousand relay stations and twenty thousand horses. Mounted couriers became a common sight, and it was no wonder people in the tiny mountain kingdom of Tibet once believed that a magical flying horse carried all their prayers to heaven.

During the Middle Ages an Asian ruler could easily send a messenger across a continent, but a European king sometimes had trouble getting a business letter to the next town. After the Roman Empire fell in A.D. 476, the old imperial postal service collapsed. Roads decayed, relay stations fell into ruins, and for the next thirteen centuries there was no safe, reliable way to send a dispatch across Europe. Although kings, merchants, and townships set up a hodgepodge of messenger services, arrangements were slipshod, and none of these organizations worked very well. All too often a hurrying courier rode his exhausted horse up to the relay station, found the stables empty, and had to kidnap a farmer's horse in order to continue his journey. On the road bandits attacked postriders. No one insisted on regular schedules, so messengers delivered mail whenever they liked. Frustrated letter writers tried to encourage postriders to provide decent service by scrawling "haste, post, haste" or "ride villain, ride for your life" on the outside of their letters, but it didn't do much good.

For over a thousand years Europeans complained about the mail system, but no one really tried to fix it—until an eighteenth-century theater owner named John Palmer made an astonishing discovery. He found that it took three days for a postrider to carry a letter from London to Bath, while an actor traveling in a public stagecoach could make the same journey in a single day.

Armed with this knowledge and tremendous determination, Mr. Palmer set out to reorganize the entire English mail service. In interview after interview he told government officials that all letters should be carried in public stagecoaches that traveled on schedule. He recommended changing horses frequently and suggested that each coach carry a driver, a guard, and several passengers. Some bureaucrats said the idea was crazy. Others called it brilliant, and finally the government agreed to give Palmer's plan a try. At 8 A.M. on August 2, 1784, four prancing horses pulled the first mail coach out of London. It traveled over a hundred miles at a fast seven miles per hour and arrived in Bristol at eleven o'clock that night. The experiment was a success, and Palmer's invention soon became the wonder of the age.

Nothing on wheels was faster than the English mail coach. The first ones traveled at six to seven miles per hour.

An English mail coach picks up the mail without stopping.
The Royal Post Office, London

Later, when roads improved, they whizzed along at a record-breaking eleven miles per hour! Cautious souls feared this phenomenally swift pace would damage passengers' health, but mail coach travelers showed no ill effects. Most of them enjoyed flying across the countryside in the brightly painted mail carriages.

Breeding coach horses became big business, and inns like the Yorkshire Grey and the Bay Horse were named after these four-legged heroes of the open road. It took only two minutes to change horses at each station. Few stops were made along the way, and to save time at pickup and delivery points the village postmaster and the coach guard tossed mailbags to each other as the coach rattled by. Occasionally, of course, mistakes occurred. In Barnet late one night the postmaster's sleepy wife accidentally tossed her husband's leather breeches to a passing coach guard instead of the leather mailbag. On the whole, however, the system was marvelously efficient, and other countries copied it.

Mail coaches were a great success in places with well-paved highways, but they weren't much use in the western part of the United States, where towns were separated by miles of wilderness and the road was often nothing more than a muddy buffalo track. Accidents, unfriendly Native Americans, and lack of organization slowed mail delivery to a crawl west of the Mississippi. Things were so bad, in fact, that in 1841 it took four months for news of President William Henry Harrison's death to travel from Washington, D.C., to California.

Westerners wanted faster service, and the owners of a freight company called Russell, Majors and Waddell thought they could provide it. On April 3, 1860, these businessmen started the most famous horse-powered postal system of all time: the Pony Express. It was actually an extremely well organized, superfast version of the ancient postrider system. Pony riders picked up letters in St. Joseph, Missouri, galloped approximately two thousand miles, and delivered the mail to Sacramento about eleven days later. Messengers changed horses at stations every 10 to 20 miles, and each man traveled 75 to 125 miles a day. It cost five dollars to send a letter, and each courier carried only twenty pounds of mail.

The Pony Express horses weren't thoroughbreds. They were tough, healthy little mustangs or Indian ponies. None weighed more than a thousand pounds, all had extremely hard hoofs, and most had very little training. One Pony Express station keeper claimed a horse was ready for use "when a rider could lead it out of the station without getting his head kicked off."

The sixty riders who carried the mail were just as tough as their mounts. They were skinny young men about eighteen years old who promised not to swear, gamble, get drunk, or mistreat animals while employed by the company. They were paid about $100 to $125 a month and were expected to risk their lives daily.

On horseback these express riders carried the mail across the scorching Nevada wastelands and through Rocky Mountain passes, where the snow was sometimes thirty-two feet deep. In lowland swamps they were almost eaten alive by swarms of hungry mosquitoes, and on desert trails they kept a sharp lookout for rattlesnakes. Native Americans sometimes shot riders or attacked stations. The relay system sometimes failed, and rider William Cody (later known as Buffalo Bill) once had to travel 322 miles without stopping.

The life was hard, but the men and horses who worked for the Pony Express did earn a place in history. In November 1860 they raced across country to tell westerners that Abraham Lincoln had been elected president. Two months later Pony Express riders were on the road again. This time

Above, U.S. postage stamp, issued in 1940, commemorating the eightieth anniversary of the founding of the Pony Express; *Right,* ad for pony express riders.

Right: The Bettmann Archive

they carried vitally important messages that kept the western states from fighting on the side of the Confederacy during the Civil War.

But even as the Pony Express riders were galloping across the plains, the service they provided was becoming obsolete. On October 24, 1861, workmen finished laying the cable for the first transcontinental telegraph line. From that day on, messages could travel from New York to San Francisco in the space of a few seconds. No horse could race against the clicking telegraph key, and after only a year of operation, the Pony Express went out of business.

History is the story of change. New inventions continually replace old, and in the twentieth century electronic communication is the order of the day. But for thousands of years horses did what telephones, radios, and communications satellites do now. They got the message through.

FINE ART
TECHNOLOGY

The Tower of Babel.
c.1563. Pieter
Bruegel the Elder.

Oil on wood.
Kunsthistorisches Museum,
Vienna. Photo: © Erich
Lessing/Art Resource

The Race Horse. 1887.
Eadweard Muybridge.

Photograph. Department of
Library Services, American
Museum of Natural History,
New York. 325907

Man on telephone with bicycle, horseback rider
in the background. c. 1930. Artist unknown.

Haveli fresco, Shekhavati district, Rajasthan, India.
Photo: © Lindsay Hebberd/Woodfin Camp & Associates

Zapotec civilization. 1942. Diego Rivera.

From a mural depicting the history of Mexico. National Palace, Mexico City.
Photo: © Robert Frerck/Woodfin Camp & Associates

GEORGE STEPHENSON

from INVENTORS by Norman Wymer
illustrated by Robert Byrd

Before the days of railways, coaches drawn by horses were the main form of public transport. The coaches were very uncomfortable and over-crowded with passengers. Some passengers were packed inside like sardines in a tin; others sat outside in the wind, rain and cold of winter.

There were no tarmac, or paved, roads. The coaches bumped along tracks riddled with ruts and potholes.

Traveling was very hazardous. A wheel might catch in a rut and turn a coach over—or highwaymen might hold up a coach with pistols and rob the passengers.

People never traveled long distances unless their journey was essential. It could take days to travel between towns far apart. A long-distance journey was made in 'stages,' and travelers spent the night at inns at the stopping places.

George Stephenson, son of a coal miner, built the first railways. He was born in 1781 in a mining village near Newcastle, England. His parents were too poor to send him to school and, as a boy, George worked in a mine, picking stones out of coal, for a wage of sixpence a day.

At the colliery his father tended an old steam engine used for pumping water out of the mine. This was the kind of job George wanted. He went to another colliery and worked as a mechanic. Gradually he climbed the ladder to better jobs until, at the age of 17, he was given charge of an engine.

Stephenson took a great pride in his engine; he dismantled it and studied its workings. He was fired with an ambition to become an engineer like James Watt, the inventor of the steam engine. His lack of education was a handicap. He would need to study engineering, but he could neither read nor write. Stephenson overcame this obstacle. In the evenings after work, a young schoolmaster taught him reading, writing and arithmetic for a penny a lesson.

Though he received no practical training, Stephenson became a skillful engineer. His great opportunity came at the age of 33. By then he was married with a son named Robert. Stephenson was in charge of the colliery's stationary engines, used for drawing up coal from the deep pits. He also supervised the transport of the coal from the colliery to the port for shipment to the customers.

Machinery was then beginning to take the place of manual labor, and factories were being built all over England. There was a great and growing demand for coal for these new factories. The trucks of coal were hauled to the port by slow, plodding horses—and a quicker method of transport was urgently needed.

Stephenson decided to construct a railway with a 'traveling engine' instead of horses to haul the trucks.

Several men had attempted to design a steam locomotive (a moving engine), based on Watt's stationary engines, but the results were disastrous. One engine overturned and nearly killed the driver; a second ran out of control and crashed into a wall; and a third blew up.

Stephenson designed and constructed a successful locomotive. It consisted of an enormous tank with a high funnel in front, like a factory chimney, through which volumes of smoke belched out, and the front and rear wheels were linked by chains, as on a bicycle. The engine ran on metal lines and it could haul eight wagons of coal, weighing 30 tons, at a speed of about 7 kilometers an hour—much faster than the horses.

Delighted by the success of his colliery railway, Stephenson looked to greater things. He declared triumphantly, "The day will soon come when people can travel by train. Railways will become the main form of transport."

In 1821 Stephenson and his son Robert—now also an engineer—began to build the world's first railway to carry passengers and goods. It ran from Stockton to Darlington, with branch lines to collieries, and the total distance was about 58 kilometers. The Stephensons built the railway in four years, and it was opened on 27 September 1825.

Thousands of people came to watch the ceremony. They expected the engine to blow up, and they came to laugh and jeer. They were far too frightened to travel on the train.

The train, with 22 open passenger cars and 6 freight cars, chugged off at a speed of 8 kilometers an hour. Stephenson drove the engine and a man with a red flag rode ahead on horseback to keep the line clear.

As the engine did not blow up, spectators along the route took courage and began to scramble aboard. Soon the train was carrying over 600 passengers.

Stephenson had a good sense of fun. "Here's your chance, George!" he chuckled to himself. "I'll show all these ladies and gentlemen what a steam engine can do!" He heaped on the coal and raised the speed to 20 kilometers an hour. The passengers cheered wildly.

After this momentous event, Stephenson was commissioned to build a second and more important railway, between Liverpool and Manchester. This was an immense

task. It involved constructing 63 bridges and a large viaduct; hewing tunnels through rocks; and laying railway lines across about 20 square kilometers of marshland, known as Chat Moss.

The decision to build this railway met with fierce opposition from the owners of canals and from farmers across whose land the railway would run. Canals then provided the main form of transport between Liverpool and Manchester and the canal companies feared that the railway would ruin their trade. The farmers protested that sparks from the engines would set fire to their crops and that the noise would stop their hens from laying eggs and their cows from producing milk.

When Stephenson and his son Robert began to survey the land, angry farmers with guns threatened to shoot them. Stephenson ignored their threats and made his survey by moonlight, when the farmers were in bed.

The survey completed, teams of workmen began to construct the bridges and hew out the tunnels. Stephenson traveled 'round on horseback and supervised their work, inspiring the men in his cheerful, confident manner.

Stephenson performed a great engineering feat in laying the railway lines across Chat Moss. This great peat bog was over 12 meters deep, and it would not bear the weight of a man, let alone a heavily-laden train. The task seemed impossible, but Stephenson worked on the principle that whereas a man will sink in water a raft will float. He decided to lay a kind of giant raft of tree trunks and brushwood

above the marshes and to build a floating railroad which, though not quite stationary, would be absolutely safe.

Load after load of tree trunks and branches was laboriously laid on the marshes to form the foundation. Gates and hurdles were placed above the trees and tons of soil and ballast were spread over the top and rammed tight. Heavy oak sleepers were pegged to this track, and the railway lines were then laid on the sleepers.

The great Duke of Wellington (then Prime Minister) opened the Liverpool–Manchester railway in September 1830, and within a few months it was carrying 1,200 passengers a day.

Stephenson's prophecy was fulfilled. During the next few years a network of railways spread like a spider's web across England, linking up the larger towns and cities—and the railways became the principal form of transport.

Stephenson, now world-famous, was asked to plan railways for foreign countries. He traveled widely and planned railway systems for several countries in Europe and for the United States of America. So the railways spread to many parts of the world.

George Stephenson—the poor boy who had no schooling—became a rich man. He died in 1848, leaving a fortune of £140,000—a very large sum of money for those days.

PROGRESS

Edith Agnew
illustrated by David Cunningham

There are two ways now
To cross the mountain.

One is a foot-path;
My father walked it beside his *burro*,
The *burro* loaded with eggs in boxes
To trade for *chile* and plums and apples
In Chimayó.

One is a highway;
Your automobile, I watch it climbing
In such a hurry, on easy curvings
That slide beneath you and wave behind you—
Pronto! You pass!

The path takes longer;
A week in going, a week in coming;
A man can see more, hear more, and feel more,
Learn more of the wisdom in long, slow thinking
Along the trail.

But, as *señor* says,
We have the highway. All the old wisdom
Does not much matter. If I could buy me
An automobile, I would not trade it
For any *burro*!

HARVEY AND HIGGINS INCORPORATED

from AMERICA TRAVELS
by Alice Dalgliesh
illustrated by Jane Kendall

J im Harvey and Dan Higgins lived in a small town in the
middle west. It was a nice town on the edge of a lake,
with pleasant houses and tree-bordered streets. Jim and
Dan lived next door to each other; they were eight and
nine years old and great friends. Jim had red hair and freck-
les and he was short and fat. Dan had brown curly hair and
blue eyes and he was tall and thin. However, although the
two boys looked so different they really were quite alike in
their ways and liked many of the same things.

One of the things that was the same about Jim and Dan was their birthday. It came on the same day, which was the thirtieth of July, right in the middle of the summer vacation. On the day that Jim was eight and Dan nine Jim woke up early. There were no presents by his bed. At the breakfast table there were no presents and no one seemed even to know that it was his birthday. After breakfast he went out in the yard and leaned over the fence to talk to Dan.

"Hullo, Dan!" said Jim.

"Hullo, Jim!" said Dan.

"I didn't get any presents for my birthday."

"I didn't either."

"Do you suppose they *forgot?*"

At that moment Jim's father came out into the Harvey backyard and Dan's father came out into the Higgins yard.

"Jim," said Mr. Harvey, "come down to the barn. I have something to show you."

"Dan," said Mr. Higgins, "come down to the barn. I have something to show you."

The barn was dark when Jim went into it and he could not see very clearly. In one stall stood Bess, the mare his father drove in the buggy. In the other stall was a small dark shape. It moved. Jim's eyes were beginning to be accustomed to the darkness and he could see that it was a pony, a very small dark-brown pony with a shaggy coat.

"What do you think of that for a birthday present?" asked his father.

"A birthday present! Dad! Is it really mine?"

His father nodded. "Take the halter and lead him out to show Danny."

Jim took the halter and led the little pony out very carefully. His heart was thumping so against his chest that he could scarcely breathe. Now he and the small brown pony were out in the sunny yard.

"Hi, Danny!" Jim's shout died off suddenly for there was Dan with a pony exactly like his own. Both fathers were watching them and laughing.

"You'll find saddles in the barn," said Mr. Harvey. "I guess you both know what to do with them."

They did. For a year the boys had wanted a pony more than anything in the world and they had practiced riding Tom Smith's pony. They had hoped only for one pony and now there were two. That day was "the best day we have had in all our lives," as Jim said to Dan. They rode the ponies and gave turns to all the children in the neighborhood.

For several weeks everything went well. Then Mr. Harvey and Mr. Higgins, who were business partners, lost a great deal of money.

"I'm afraid the ponies will have to go," said Mr. Harvey. "They cost a good deal to keep and I am selling Bessie."

"Oh, Dad, can't we keep them? Can't we keep them if Dan and I earn the money to feed them?"

"Well, perhaps, but how can you earn the money?"

"We'll think of a way."

So Jim and Dan thought and thought, but they could not think of a plan. At last an idea came to Danny.

"Jim, I know! Let's fix up our wagon and deliver things for the stores."

"Could we, would they let us?"

"They'll have to. Come on!"

The wagon in which the boys sometimes drove their ponies was fixed up. The boys painted it a very bright blue. On each side of it they painted in rather crooked letters:

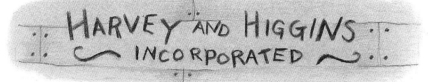

"Partners are 'incorporated,'" said Jim who had seen the word on their fathers' office door.

"I don't know exactly what it means, but anyway it looks well on the wagon," said Dan.

So Harvey and Higgins were started in business, and it was surprising how the business grew. At first they delivered a few packages for the hardware store. Then they took flowers for the florist. Soon the smaller stores began to find out that people liked to have the blue wagon and the two small ponies trot up to their door and deliver a package. So the boys found that each day after school there were interesting packages to be taken to houses all over the town.

One afternoon Harvey and Higgins left the bakers with a most exciting package. There were other packages, too, but placed very carefully in the middle of the wagon was a large box done up in white paper and tied with an enormous silvery bow. It was Dorothea May Armstrong's birthday cake. Dorothea May lived in the largest house in town, a house to which Harvey and Higgins had always wanted to deliver a package.

"Do you suppose they'll ask us to take it in?" asked Jim as they drove carefully along Main Street. "I've always wanted to see inside that house."

"Maybe they will," said Danny. "Look, Jim! What's the crowd on the corner over by the hotel?"

"Let's drive over and see," said Jim.

Over by the hotel a crowd had gathered and was staring curiously at a large black object.

"It's one of those new horseless carriages!" said Dan excitedly. "We never saw one here before. Let's go nearer." So they drove nearer. The strange black carriage was making queer, purring sounds. It coughed, it snorted, it choked. The crowd laughed. The tall man who sat in it looked annoyed. He climbed out and turned a handle in the front of the machine, ran back, climbed in, turned something else, and the machine leaped forward with a mighty roar that scattered the crowd and made the babies burst into surprised howls.

And the ponies of Harvey and Higgins Incorporated! Never had they seen anything like the noisy black object!

Like twin streaks of lightning off they went along Main Street with Harvey shouting, "Whoa!" and Higgins hanging on to the lines. Packages were scattered everywhere. When finally the ponies came to a standstill heaving and sweating and rolling their terrified eyes, Dan and Jim looked blankly at each other.

"The birthday cake!"

Sadly they went back along Main Street walking beside the ponies. Friendly onlookers handed them the packages, some decidedly the worse for wear. Close by the hotel a boy who was in Dan's class at school held the large silver-ribboned package in his arms.

"Hey, Danny! This slid off just as you started. I caught it!"

Dan and Jim heaved sighs of relief. "Maybe it isn't hurt." They untied the box carefully and peered into the package. A dozen or so boys and girls gathered around and peered too. There was the cake quite unharmed, glittering with

its white frosting and pink flowers and silver trimmings. It was safe!

Then Dan happened to look up at the clock. Three forty-five, and the party was to be at four! The Armstrong house was at the other end of town. They couldn't make it. For the first time Harvey and Higgins would fail to deliver a package and so would be utterly disgraced.

"Well, boys! I'm sorry my automobile scared your ponies," said a voice. "I'll make it good with you about those packages."

They looked up to see the owner of the car that had made the trouble. He looked so friendly that in a minute they were telling him the whole sad tale of the birthday cake.

"Can't deliver it, you say? Why not? There's my machine right around the corner, it'll get us there in two shakes of a lamb's tail. Get a boy to drive your ponies home and off we'll go. You'll be the first boys in this town to ride in an automobile!"

The first boys in the town to ride in an automobile! Harvey and Higgins could scarcely believe it was not a dream. There they were, rattling along Main Street, Danny holding the box with the cake very carefully on his knees. People stood still on the sidewalks to look at them. Jim hoped that none of the boys in his class would miss the sight. The first boys in the town to ride in a horseless carriage! He wondered if it were very dangerous, but he did not much care if it were.

There was a bang and a clatter. The machine stopped short and no amount of coaxing would make it go. The gentleman got out, lifted the hood in front and peered inside. Then he came back, got a tool and fussed with the machinery. It seemed a long time before the car was ready to start.

"I think we could have got there quicker with our ponies!" whispered Jim to Dan.

A crowd of small boys gathered to watch what was going on. They snickered and giggled.

"Get a horse!" suggested one of the boys. Then they all joined in chanting loudly in chorus:

"Get a horse, Mister! Get a horse!"

Suddenly when the car was cranked something inside it began to purr softly. With a cough and a snort they were off again!

In no time at all they were puffing and snorting up the driveway of the Armstrong home. The butler came out of the house, his eyes almost popping out of his head. Dorothea May came running out too.

"Oh, Daddy! Mother! Bob! Susan!" she called. "Here's one of those queer new carriages."

The whole Armstrong family came out and stood on the doorstep. Danny climbed out of the car with a great deal of dignity and handed the large box to Dorothea May. "Your birthday cake!" he said. "A little late, I'm afraid, but it might never have got here at all." Then he climbed into the car again and off they puffed and snorted down the drive.

"I'm glad the ponies ran away!" whispered Jim to Dan. "If they hadn't run away we wouldn't have been the first boys in this town to ride in this machine."

Now Jim and Dan are grown up and in that very same town there is a handsome dark-blue delivery truck with HARVEY AND HIGGINS INCORPORATED painted on it in the neatest letters. Harvey and Higgins don't drive the truck themselves, though sometimes they look out of their office windows and wish that they did. It was such fun in the old days when they drove down Main Street in the blue wagon behind the two little brown ponies!

BIBLIOGRAPHY

Black Beauty by Anna Sewell. Can a horse talk? Black Beauty, a brave and beautiful London horse, tells his life story.

City: A Story of Roman Planning and Construction by David Macaulay. Read how the ancient Romans built their cities, step by step.

Faster Than a Horse: Moving West with Engine Power by Suzanne Hilton. Learn how railroads replaced horses and changed the way people traveled.

Homer Price by Robert McCloskey. Not all new inventions are helpful. When Homer encounters a new doughnut machine, the results are hilarious!

Paul Revere's Ride by Henry Wadsworth Longfellow. This famous poem retells the story of Revere's daring midnight ride through the Boston countryside to warn the colonists that the British were coming.

Once Upon A Horse by Suzanne Jurmain. How have horses been used by man throughout history? Read and discover the exciting facts!

The Story of the Pony Express by R. Conrad Stein. Bravery, courage, and dedication described the young men who delivered mail on horseback in the 1800s.

Watt Got You Started, Mr. Fulton? A Story of James Watt & Robert Fulton by Robert Quackenbush. In this double biography, you will learn how the steam engine and the steamboat replaced horses.

VIRGINIA SETTLEMENT

Ba

ALGONQUIN

Jamestown

Iroquois Nation

MOHAWK

ONEIDA
ONONDAGA
CAYUGA
SENECA

50

ADKINS

Raleigh

DUGOUT CANOE

Charleston

TOBACCO TRADING

BRITISH COLONIAL TROOPS

204

VIRGINIA LEAF

COLONIAL LIFE

EARLY AMERICA
Trevor Matheney

When the colonists arrived in America, they were beginning a new life in what to them was a "new world." They weren't completely aware of the long and varied history of the place they called the Americas.

There is evidence that long before Columbus in 1492 or John Cabot in 1497 ever set foot in the Americas, nomadic groups had traveled from Asia and spread out through what is now the United States and South America. These people formed tribes such as the Hopewell and Powhatan and great civilizations such as the Aztec and Inca. In addition, artifacts that have been found suggest visits by the Japanese, Chinese, and Phoenicians.

By the early 1500s many Spanish, English, French, and Portuguese explorers, fishermen, and traders were traveling to the Americas and returning with tales of giant forests, huge stretches of land, and plenty of clear blue waters.

This was particularly interesting to European men. For the most part in Europe at that time, only the oldest son could inherit the land of his father. Thus, for many younger sons the only way to have land of their own was to leave Europe. The idea of settling in the New World of the Americas became very attractive.

Other people wanted to escape some of the problems they faced in Europe. In many places in Europe, people were not allowed religious freedom. Some of these people felt they would be able to worship as they pleased in the New World.

Spain and England were the first countries to build settlements in the Americas. These settlements were called colonies. The first Spanish settlement was established at St. Augustine, Florida, in 1565.

St. Augustine Foundation at Flagler College

In 1585, the English began a colony on Roanoke Island off the coast of what is now North Carolina. This colony failed. However, another attempt to colonize Roanoke Island was made in 1587. It was here that Virginia Dare, the first English child born in America, was born. In 1590, when supply ships returned from England to the Roanoke Colony, everyone had disappeared. No one knows what happened to these early colonists. Because of this, the Roanoke Colony has become known as the Lost Colony.

The Jamestown Colony, founded in 1607, and the Plymouth Colony, founded in 1620, were the first two English colonies that survived. The Jamestown Colony grew into what was called the Virginia Colony. The Plymouth Colony was located in what is now Massachusetts and is where the Pilgrims first settled.

The colonists had to face the hardships of living in a new, unfamiliar land. Many died of disease or starvation. Most of the early colonists were farmers, growing corn, beans, and other food and raising their own animals. They made their own clothes, built their own homes, and worked long, hard days. Few colonial children went to school. Often parents used the Bible to teach their children to read. A few colleges were eventually started for men only. The first college in the colonies was Harvard, founded in 1636 in Massachusetts.

The Native Americans helped these early colonists survive their first years in the New World. However, some Native American groups were upset at having their lands taken by these new people who often brought with them unfriendly ways and diseases deadly to the Native Americans. As more and more colonists arrived, they began taking land from these groups. Several wars were fought between the colonists and the Native Americans. In 1675, a Native American leader named King Philip led the Wampanoag and Narragansett tribes in a war against the colonists in Massachusetts and Rhode Island. These were the same tribes who had helped the colonists survive their first years in the New World. Now, they were angry. Both tribes were nearly destroyed in this war. Clashes between the colonists and the Native Americans continued throughout the colonial period.

North Wind Picture Archives

Although the colonies were governed by England, not all colonists were English. Many were from Germany, France, the Netherlands, Sweden, Ireland, and Scotland. Others were brought from Africa as indentured servants and later, slaves. By 1700 there were about 250,000 colonists living in the thirteen English colonies in America.

The colonies were different in many ways. For example, in Massachusetts, most of the colonists came as families looking for land to settle. The Rhode Island and Pennsylvania colonies were settled by religious groups in search of freedom to worship as they pleased. The New York Colony became the most culturally and ethnically diverse colony. People from all countries began to settle there.

Many of the early colonists were unmarried men under the age of twenty-five. In the Maryland Colony, most colonists were single men who arrived as indentured servants. They would work for a period of time, up to seven years, before being given their freedom. In exchange, they received food and shelter, and often learned a trade. Over half of these Maryland colonists died of starvation and disease within a few years of arriving in the colonies.

As the number of indentured servants decreased, there was a shortage of workers in the colonies. To fill this shortage, the colonists turned to slavery. In some colonies, over one-fourth of the population consisted of African slaves. However, not all colonial Africans were slaves. Some had come to America as indentured servants and when their indenture was served they were free to work as they saw fit.

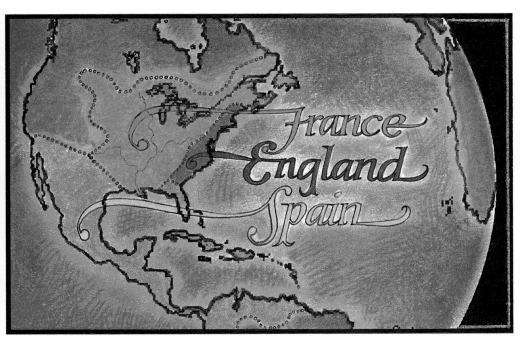

England was not the only country to own land in America. Spain owned what is now Florida, and France owned much of the land west of the thirteen English colonies. This prevented the English colonists from spreading out. Because of this, the population in the English colonies became more concentrated. Cities and towns grew out of the early settlements.

The colonists began to feel they lived in a country so different from England that English law and the English government no longer served them well. These ideas would lead to the Revolutionary War, in which the thirteen English colonies would become the United States of America.

JAMESTOWN:
FIRST PERMANENT ENGLISH SETTLEMENT IN AMERICA
from THE VIRGINIA COLONY
by Dennis B. Fradin

As the three ships that were carrying the English-men sailed up the river that they called the James, some Native Americans who called the same river the Powhatan were watching them. It is possible that some of these people had seen Europeans before. In 1570, Span-ish missionaries had built a settlement in Virginia that the Native Americans quickly destroyed. Later the English sent out several ships to explore the coast of what is now the eastern United States. These explorers named this land Virginia, in honor of their Virgin Queen, Elizabeth I. However, the explorers of the late 1500s failed to set up any permanent settlements in Virginia or anywhere else in America.

The Native Americans watched from the forest as the Englishmen left their ships to explore. On one of their first landings, at a point that the English called Cape Henry, about thirty colonists were attacked by a small band of Native Americans.

Queen Elizabeth I
(1533–1603)

According to Captain John Smith, the Native Americans "hurt two of the English very dangerously."

To understand why the Native Americans attacked the English, it might help to reverse the situation. Pretend you lived in a village in England. What if, in the spring of 1607, a hundred Native Americans with weapons arrived at your village and took land from you without asking permission? Would you fight?

To the Native Americans, the men who had arrived in the three "floating islands" and who were armed with "thunder-sticks" were invaders. They were the enemy.

The three English ships—which were named the *Susan Constant*, the *Godspeed*, and the *Discovery*—continued up the James River for about sixty miles. Finally, on May 14, 1607, the colonists reached a small peninsula on the river's

Nineteenth-century drawing gives an idealized picture of the English landing at Jamestown.

Historical Pictures/Stock Montage

north side. They walked onto the marshy shore, looked around, and decided that this was a good place to build a fort. Here they could defend themselves from attack by either the Spanish or the Native Americans. They soon began work on their settlement, which they called Jamestown after King James I. Jamestown was to be the first permanent English settlement in America.

The colonists had been sent to Virginia by a group of wealthy London merchants called the Virginia Company of London. The London merchants hoped that the Virginia colonists would discover gold and other treasures, which they would ship back to England.

The colonists had made the long and dangerous voyage across the Atlantic Ocean for many reasons. Because

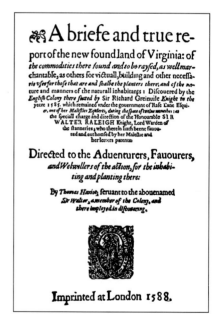

Books were written to encourage English settlers to travel to the newly discovered land called Virginia.

English laws at that time favored the oldest son, the younger children of wealthy families often inherited very little of their parents' land and possessions. Some of the colonists were younger sons who wanted land, which they could never have in their home country. Others were hungry for the gold that the London Company hoped would be found in Virginia. Still others wanted to introduce Christianity to the Native Americans. Finally, some were adventurers who were looking for excitement at the edge of the known world.

Before the ships had sailed, the names of the seven men who were to govern the colony were placed in a sealed box by the directors of the London Company. The box remained sealed until the men reached Virginia. When the box was opened, the colonists were not surprised by six of the names: Christopher Newport, the captain of the *Susan Constant*; Bartholomew Gosnold, captain of the *Godspeed*; John Ratcliffe, captain of the *Discovery*; John Martin, a sea captain who had once sailed with the great English explorer Sir Francis Drake; Edward Maria Wingfield, an investor in the London Company; and George Kendall, another sea captain. The seventh name, however, was a surprise. It belonged to a man who was neither a sea captain nor what the English thought to be a "gentleman." His name was John

A replica of the *Godspeed* can be visited in restored Jamestown.

Smith, and he had spent most of the Atlantic voyage locked in irons after quarreling with Edward Wingfield.

The red-haired, blue-eyed, twenty-seven-year-old Smith had already lived through many adventures as a soldier of fortune in such places as the Netherlands, Hungary, and Romania. While fighting with the Hungarian army, Smith was wounded, then taken to Turkey as a slave. After escaping, he made his way back to England by late 1604. Growing restless after several years at home, Smith decided that the New World was the place for him to make his fame and fortune. He joined the London Company's Virginia expedition.

Despite the orders from the London Company, the other men on the governing council refused to admit John

Captain John Smith (1580–1631) and his coat of arms.

North Wind Picture Archives, Historical Pictures/Stock Montage

Smith. However, Smith soon proved that he was the man who was best able to help the colony survive.

Many of the Englishmen who came to Virginia were used to having servants do things for them. They were not very good at farming, working with their hands, or dealing with other people. Smith could do these things quite well. Smith also had the best military sense among the colonists.

In May of 1607, the governing council decided that about twenty men, including Smith, should explore the James River. Captain Smith protested that it was more important for the colonists to finish building the fort at Jamestown. They needed its protection. But the council

This advertisement from the Virginia Company of London reported on the fertile land in Virginia.
New York Public Library

Unfortunately few of the first settlers of Jamestown were farmers or carpenters. They were accustomed to having others do this kind of work.
The Bettmann Archive

ruled against Smith. Then, while he and the others were off exploring, Native Americans attacked the unfinished fort, killed two colonists, and wounded ten others. Several weeks after this tragic event, Smith was admitted to the governing council. He was soon recognized as the leader of the colony.

Under John Smith's direction the fort was completed by mid-June of 1607. Smith then had the men build the town's first thatch-roofed houses. Although the building went well, the colonists faced several big problems.

By the summer of 1607 the colony was running short of food. The Englishmen had planned to arrive in Virginia in time to plant crops, but the trip had taken longer than expected. It was too late to plant crops. The colonists tried to hunt and fish, but nearly all of them, except John Smith, were not able to do it. In the midst of a land full of wildlife and plant foods, the Jamestown colonists suffered from famine.

Disease was another terrible problem. Although the location of Jamestown was good for military reasons, it was very bad for health reasons. The drinking water was polluted, and the marshes near Jamestown were a breeding ground for mosquitoes. As a result, the colonists caught malaria, pneumonia, dysentery, and other diseases. By the end of the summer of 1607, almost half the Jamestown colonists were dead, and many more were dying.

From time to time the Native Americans came to the settlement with meat and corn, which they traded to the

John Smith trading with the Native Americans.
Historical Pictures/Stock Montage

colonists for various trinkets. But the Englishmen could not get enough food from them. John Smith realized that, if any of the Englishmen were to survive their first winter in Virginia, they would need to get large amounts of food from the Native Americans.

Smith led several food expeditions. Loaded down with mirrors, beads, and trinkets, Smith and a few other men would walk into a Native American village and bargain with them for deer meat, corn, and bread. Because the Native Americans did not trust the whites, these trading expeditions were quite dangerous.

In late December of 1607, John Smith was seeking food near the Chickahominy River when he and his little band were suddenly attacked by men of the Powhatan tribe. Several of the colonists were killed, and Smith was taken prisoner.

Smith could tell that the Powhatans were thinking of killing him right away. To gain time, he pulled out his compass, and, speaking to the men in their own language, demonstrated how the needle always pointed to the north. The Native Americans decided to spare this fascinating man for a while. They took him to the village where Chief Powhatan (the tribe and their chief were both called Powhatan) was staying.

After being led into Powhatan's lodge, Smith was questioned by the chief. Powhatan wanted to know why the Englishmen were in Virginia and when they would leave. Smith tried to lie his way out of trouble by saying that they had been driven there by a storm and would soon be leaving. Powhatan didn't believe him. Smith was sentenced to die for killing two Native Americans at the Chickahominy River battle.

Upon Powhatan's signal, two large stones were brought forth. The Native Americans grabbed John Smith, threw him to the ground, and forced his head onto the stones. When several men raised their clubs above his head,

Pomejack, Powhatan's village

Historical Pictures/Stock Montage

Pocahontas
rescues
John Smith.

Smith was certain that the end was near. But then the
chief's daughter Pocahontas, who was about twelve years
old, ran to Captain Smith and cradled his head in her arms.

Although John Smith thought that Pocahontas had saved
him on impulse, many historians think that the Native
Americans did not really mean to kill Smith. They think
that this dramatic event symbolized Pocahontas's "adoption"
of the captain. Either way it is probable that Smith was
saved because Pocahontas had taken a liking to him.

Smith exchanged pledges of friendship with Powhatan
and then was escorted home. After this, Powhatan traded
food to the colonists. He also taught them how to plant corn
and make fishing traps. The settlers needed this help very
much because, by the time Captain Smith returned to
Jamestown in early January of 1608, only about forty of the
original one hundred colonists were still living.

POCAHONTAS

from THE VIRGINIA COLONY
by Dennis B. Fradin
illustrated by Robert Roth

Ætatis suæ 21. A. 1616.

Matoaks als Rebecka daughter to the mighty Prince
Powhatan Emperour of Attanoughkomouck als Virginia
converted and baptized in the Christian faith, and
Wife to the wor.ll M.r Tho: Rolff.

This painting of Pocahontas, done while she was touring England
shortly before her death, shows her in English clothing.

Exactly when and where the Native American girl named Matoaka was born is not known, but it probably was in eastern Virginia around 1595. When the Jamestown colonists arrived in 1607, Matoaka was about twelve years old. Little is known about Matoaka's life away from the colonists, but when she was with them, she lived up to her nickname, Pocahontas, which means "The Playful One."

After Pocahontas saved John Smith's life, there was a short time of peace between the colonists and the Native Americans. During this time Pocahontas often came to Jamestown, where she would challenge the young men to compete with her at performing handsprings and running races. The English youths taught her a phrase: "Love you not me?" which Pocahontas would repeat to them. In return, Pocahontas taught Captain Smith and the other colonists some Native American words.

In the spring of 1608, John Smith got into an argument with Pocahontas's people during a bargaining session and took seven of them captive. Powhatan tried to get the prisoners released, but nothing worked until he sent Pocahontas to Jamestown as his agent. Captain Smith and the other leaders of Jamestown let the prisoners go for the sake of Pocahontas.

About a year after this incident, Smith left Virginia, and relations between the Native Americans and the colonists worsened. Those few times when the Native Americans and the colonists met peacefully, Pocahontas and her people asked what had become of Captain Smith. The colonists always said that he was dead.

In 1613 Pocahontas was staying in a Native American village along the Potomac River when she was kidnapped and taken first to Jamestown and then to Henrico. In Henrico she was given fancy English petticoats and dresses to replace her deerskin clothes, taught the English language, and renamed Rebecca. How Pocahontas felt about this we do not know. We do know, however, that Pocahontas met the tobacco planter John Rolfe in the summer of 1613 and that the next spring the two were married in a ceremony that was Jamestown's big social event of the year.

In 1616 Pocahontas and her husband went with their year-old son, Thomas, and several other Native Americans to England. She was introduced to royalty and invited to balls and banquets. In England, Pocahontas also learned a startling piece of news: John Smith was still alive! One day in the fall of 1616 Captain Smith called at the house where she was staying near London.

Pocahontas, who by this time was ill because of England's damp and chilly weather, was both pleased and upset at the sight of Smith. "They did tell us always you were dead," she said. Pocahontas then teased Smith for having forgotten her, reminded him that she had adopted him long

ago, and called him "Father." When Smith said that she should not call him "Father," Pocahontas answered, "I tell you then I will, and I will be forever and ever your countryman."

A few minutes later Captain Smith left, and the two never met again. In March of 1617, just as the Rolfes were about to sail home to Virginia, Pocahontas died of small-pox. The woman who had saved John Smith's life and who had once performed handsprings in Jamestown was only twenty-two years old when she died. Thomas Rolfe, her son, was educated in England. At age twenty he returned to Virginia, where he became a popular citizen and even helped defend the colony against the Native Americans.

FIRST CONFLICTS AND SHARP BEGINNINGS

Duane Damon

illustrated by Charles Shaw

E yes bright and eager, seventeen-year-old William Bradford listened intently to the speaker. The commanding voice of the white-bearded Reverend Richard Clyfton filled the room, and William did not want to miss a word. After all, he had put up with much just to attend this meeting. The neighborhood boys had taunted him as he walked past that morning. At home, his uncles were angry with him. Even here in the tiny village of Scrooby, England, being a Separatist was not easy.

William Brewster knew the risks only too well. Brewster was master of the manor house where this small band of forty-odd Separatists had gathered for more than a year. Because of his beliefs, he had recently lost his job as Scrooby postmaster. Soon he was to face arrest and trial, for Brewster and the other Scrooby Separatists were committing an illegal and dangerous act. They were worshiping God as they, not the king, believed was right.

In the England of 1607, this was a serious offense. The Church of England was an institution of immense wealth and power. Like other British monarchs before him, King James I controlled the Church. People who ignored the Church's rulings were hounded, imprisoned, tortured, or even hanged.

But change was coming. King James had authorized new translations of the Latin Bible, and literacy was spreading. As more common people were able to study the Bible for themselves, they began to question the practices of the Church.

Some wanted the Church of England cleansed of its undesirable elements, or purified. These Puritans hated the lavish rituals of the Church. They rejected the idea of stern priests and powerful bishops in fancy robes. Many Puritans were content to work for gradual change, but others were not. One group believed that the only hope for their way of worship lay in separating from the Church of England. These dissenters were called Separatists.

James I was alarmed. If people could challenge the authority of the Church, what could stop them from challenging his power as king? Acting quickly, James outlawed all private prayer meetings and independent congregations. No one who defied the Church of England was allowed to leave the country.

Fear spread through Separatist groups in Scrooby and across England. Neighbors began to ridicule and spy on them. Local merchants refused to do business with them. William Brewster was stripped of his position as postmaster. Soon afterward, he and three others were hauled into court and fined.

Worse still, "some were taken and clapped up in prison," William Bradford later wrote. "Others had their houses beset and watched night and day." The situation had become intolerable.

By late 1607, a fateful decision faced the members of the Scrooby congregation, who had begun to refer to themselves as Saints. While young William Bradford listened, Brewster, Reverend Clyfton, "radical" preacher John Robinson, and others debated. "By a joint consent," recorded Bradford, "they resolved to go into the Low Countries, where they heard was Freedom of Religion for all Men." Other Separatist groups had already fled to Holland. Now, weary of persecution, the Saints prepared to do the same.

But escape held grave dangers of its own. In the coastal town of Boston, England, the Scrooby leaders found an English ship's master who agreed to help them. The congregation shouldered its few belongings and trudged some sixty miles to meet their ship. No sooner had the members boarded than the Saints discovered they had been betrayed.

They were seized by constables, shoved into boats, and searched. Next they were paraded in shame through the streets of Boston while a hostile crowd whistled and jeered. Humiliated, the Scrooby Separatists—men, women, and children—were thrown into jail. Within a month or two, all were released.

By the spring of 1608, they were ready to try again. This time the Separatists hired a Dutch captain in the seaport of Hull to sail them to Holland. Women, children, and possessions were loaded into a small boat and floated down river and stream to the rendezvous point. The men traveled overland on foot. Arriving first, the boat became mired in a nearby creek.

When the men arrived, they were dismayed to find the women and children huddled aboard the stranded boat. When the Dutchman's ship appeared, he dispatched a dinghy to pick up the men. William Bradford was among the first boatload brought aboard.

Suddenly a large mob appeared on the shore. Brandishing guns and clubs, the mob headed straight for the marooned women and children. The startled Dutch captain weighed anchor and sailed away.

"The poor men which were got aboard were in great distress for their wives and children," Bradford recalled. "It drew tears from their eyes." They could only watch helplessly as their families and the remaining men were arrested and taken away. Among the captives were Brewster and Clyfton.

Once in town, the Separatists were hustled from one judge to another. Ironically, no one knew what to do with this pathetic band. At last, the group was released to return to homes they no longer had.

Meanwhile, Bradford and the others aboard the Dutch ship had their own trials to endure. A terrible storm blew up and for days battered the vessel. Time and again, the Dutchman's crew believed the ship was doomed. After two perilous weeks, they managed to dock safely in Amsterdam.

Back in England, Brewster and Clyfton worked tirelessly to help the last Separatists get to Holland. "And though some few shrunk at these first conflicts and sharp beginnings," wrote Bradford, "yet many more came on with fresh courage." By the summer of 1608, all the Scrooby Separatists were reunited in their new country.

After a year in Amsterdam, the Separatists moved to the city of Leyden. Here their new lives began in earnest.

With its gabled stone houses and wandering canals, Leyden was an inviting place to live. Men and women could worship God as they pleased. At the nearby University of Leyden, students and teachers could debate politics and religion freely. The Separatists had found religious freedom, but all was not perfect.

For one thing, Leyden was a center of cloth making and other city trades. The Scrooby Separatists were country folk. They became discouraged with toiling long hours indoors for low pay as weavers, cobblers, and tailors.

Second, the stricter older members disapproved of the freer, looser style of living in Holland. Parents worried that their children would grow up more Dutch than English.

If Holland was not right for them, what place was? After much discussion, the Separatists chose America. Many feared the dangers of an Atlantic crossing and an unknown land, however, and in the end, fewer than fifty of the congregation decided to risk the first journey. The rest would follow later.

Where would they get the money to go? After many months, an English businessman named Thomas Weston approached the Separatists with an offer. He would assemble a group of seventy London merchant speculators, or Adventurers, to finance their venture. In return, the Separatists would establish an English colony and ship goods such as fish and lumber back to England.

In July 1620, the Separatists said good-bye to Leyden. After eleven years, "they left that goodly and pleasant city," wrote William Bradford, "and knew that they were pilgrims."

THE VOYAGE OF THE MAYFLOWER

Patricia M. Whalen

illustrated by Charles Shaw

Pelted by rain under a black sky, the ninety-foot *Mayflower* rolled and pitched on mountainous waves. Its masts were bare because during a storm, a sailing ship must lower all its sails and drift with the wind to avoid capsizing or breaking apart.

Below the main deck, the passengers huddled in the dark. They could hear the wind howling and the waves thudding against the vessel's wooden sides and washing over the deck. Seawater dripped down on them through the canvas covering the deck gratings and seeped through the seams in the planking. The passengers were soaked and shivering; several were seasick besides. As frightened adults tried to comfort terrified children, they prayed for safety in the storm and an end to the long, terrible voyage.

Suddenly, above the din of the storm, they heard the noise of splitting timber. One of the beams supporting the deck had cracked! The ship was in danger of sinking. Then

234

someone remembered a great iron screw brought from Holland. Carefully, the ship's carpenter positioned it beneath the beam and braced it. It would hold; the passengers and crew could reach land safely.

Crossing the Atlantic in 1620 was extremely risky. A wooden ship could leak or break apart in a storm. Since the sails could be raised only in fair weather, it was impossible to predict how long a voyage would last. To avoid the stormy autumn months, ships usually made the crossing in spring or summer. They almost never sailed alone.

Aware of these dangers, the Pilgrims had planned to cross the ocean in two ships in the summer of 1620. The English Separatists from Holland (who called themselves Saints) borrowed money from London businessmen and purchased a small ship, the *Speedwell*. For the Separatists' safety, and to help them establish a profitable colony, the businessmen recruited additional volunteers in London.

The businessmen rented the *Mayflower*, a ship three times the size of the *Speedwell*, for these recruits, whom the Separatists called Strangers. The Saints and Strangers met for the first time in Southampton, England, a few days before the ships sailed on August 5.

The tiny *Speedwell* had been refitted with taller masts and larger sails so it could keep up with the *Mayflower*. These changes, however, caused the ship to leak badly at sea. On August 12, the ships put into Dartmouth. After the *Speedwell* was examined and repaired, they set off again on August 23. Two days later, the *Speedwell* began to leak again, and the vessels headed for Plymouth, England. There the ships' masters, carpenters, and principal passengers agreed that the *Speedwell* could not make the crossing.

Over the next few days, the sixty-seven Strangers on the *Mayflower* made room for thirty-five of the Saints from the *Speedwell*, along with their belongings and provisions. On September 6, the *Mayflower* set out from Plymouth alone. The one hundred two passengers, including thirty-four children, would not see land for sixty-six days.

The *Mayflower*, like all ships of the time, was built to carry cargo, not passengers. A few families crowded into the "great cabbin" in the stern. Most of the passengers, however, traveled in bunks or tiny "cabbins" below the main deck and above the hold, where cargo was stored. In this "'tween decks" area, they had only five feet of head room. Each person's living space was smaller than the mattress of a modern twin bed.

Mayflower

Speedwell

The Pilgrims suffered other discomforts. Many were seasick, particularly at the beginning of the voyage. In storms, they were constantly wet and cold. They could not bathe or wash and dry their clothes and bedding. For toilet purposes, they used buckets.

In fair weather, the adults and children who had recovered from seasickness could leave their dim, foul-smelling quarters for the wind and spray of the main deck. The adults took deep breaths of the cold, tangy air and stretched cramped muscles. The younger children, forbidden to run around, played quiet games. Damaris Hopkins, age three, and Mary and Remember Allerton, ages four and six, "tended the baby" (played with dolls). Six- and nine-year-old brothers Wrestling and Love Brewster played "I Spy" and "Hunt the Slipper" with six- and seven-year-old Jasper and Richard More. Finger games such as cat's cradle and paper, scissors, stone were popular with eight-year-old Humility Cooper, Ellen More, John Cooke, John Billington, and Bartholomew Allerton. Elizabeth Tilley, age fourteen, and Mary Chilton and Constance Hopkins, both fifteen, helped prepare the meals.

For cooking, the passengers built charcoal fires in metal braziers set in sandboxes. There was so little space, however, that only a few people could cook at once. When storms made lighting fires dangerous, everyone ate cold meals.

After morning prayers, they ate a simple breakfast of cheese and ship's biscuit (hard, dry biscuit). If cooking was allowed, they might have porridge. Their midday meal might consist of ship's biscuit and cheese or, in fair weather, cooked "pease pottage," boiled salt fish, pork, or beef and any freshly caught bonito or porpoise. Before retiring, they had a light supper. Everyone, even the children, drank beer with their meals because it was preferred to water.

Not until December 11, more than a month after first sighting land, did the Pilgrims decide where they would build their colony. One day, before an exploring party left the *Mayflower*, the passengers and crew had another narrow escape. In his family's "cabbin," fourteen-year-old Francis Billington tried making "squibs" (small fireworks) by lighting short pieces of rope. He then fired a couple of muskets and a fowling piece near an open, half-full barrel of gunpowder. No one knows why his mischief did not blow up the ship.

The *Mayflower* remained anchored offshore during the winter while the Pilgrims built their new homes. On April 5, 1621, the ship set sail for England. With the prevailing winds and currents, it made the return trip in only thirty-one days.

THE MASSACHUSETTS COLONY

Dennis B. Fradin

Conditions were terrible for the Pilgrims during their first winter at Plymouth. The men who were building the town had to brave the cold and the snow. Those still living aboard the *Mayflower* had it almost as bad. Before December ended half a dozen Pilgrims had died of disease—possibly typhus or scurvy. Each month during that winter, disease killed another ten or twelve people. By winter's end, only about fifty of the colonists were still alive.

By the early spring of 1621 Native Americans had gathered near Plymouth. Each day they came a little nearer—whether out of curiosity or as preparation for an attack the Pilgrims did not know. The few surviving men were in the common house discussing what to do if the Native Americans attacked when Samoset, a Wampanoag Indian living in the area, suddenly walked into Plymouth saying, "Welcome, Englishmen!"

Samoset, who had learned English from fishermen in Maine, was so friendly that he eased the colonists' fear of Native Americans. He told the Pilgrims about the land and people of Massachusetts. They shared their dinner of duck, biscuits, cheese, and pudding with him. Samoset spent the night in the house of Elizabeth and Stephen Hopkins, the parents of Oceanus, who was born on the *Mayflower*.

The next day Samoset left Plymouth, but he soon returned with five other Wampanoags. These five brought with them some tools which had been stolen from the Pilgrims' hiding place in the woods. The return of their tools greatly cheered the Pilgrims, for it showed that the Native Americans wanted to be friendly. The five other Wampanoags sang and danced for the Pilgrims and then left, but Samoset once again stayed the night with his new friends. Before saying good-bye, Samoset said that next time he would bring Squanto, a Native American who knew English even better than himself because he had been to England.

Samoset welcomes the Pilgrims and offers to help them.

The New England, Boston, Massachusetts

Squanto meets with the Pilgrims.

As promised, the next day Samoset returned with Squanto, who was the sole survivor of the Patuxet tribe. Samoset and Squanto explained that Chief Massasoit was nearby and wanted to meet the Pilgrims. A peaceful meeting with Massasoit was important, for he was chief of the Wampanoags. His tribe controlled southeastern Massachusetts, including the spot where Plymouth was located. Squanto went back and forth between the Wampanoags and the Pilgrim leaders to arrange a meeting. Finally, Massasoit and twenty of his men put their weapons aside and marched into Plymouth. Captain Standish escorted Massasoit into a house, and there the Wampanoag chief met John Carver, the Plymouth Colony governor.

The Native Americans had many reasons to dislike the English. For one thing, the English had built a settlement without asking permission. Also, Massasoit and his people knew that Native Americans had been mistreated by other Europeans in the past. They had been tricked in trade, carried off to Europe as prisoners, and sometimes shot without cause. For all these reasons, it would not have been surprising if Massasoit had ordered the Pilgrims to leave.

Instead, Governor Carver was pleased to find that Massasoit wanted to be friends. Some historians think that

The Pilgrims agree to a peace treaty with Massasoit.
Historical Pictures/Stock Montage

Massasoit wanted the powerful English as allies in case of war with other tribes. Others say that Massasoit was a generous man who did not mind sharing the land with the English. Whatever the reason, Carver and Massasoit exchanged kisses and shared a drink as tokens of friendship. After that, the two leaders went to work.

Carver and Massasoit agreed that their people would not carry weapons in each other's presence. Also, each group would aid the other in case of attack by a third party. Massasoit then took out his tobacco, and the two leaders smoked the peace pipe. The peace treaty that John Carver and Massasoit agreed to on that spring day in 1621 lasted for more than fifty years.

Squanto's friendship proved to be just as important as Massasoit's to the Pilgrims. Since his own people were dead,

Squanto taught the Pilgrims how to plant corn.

Historical Pictures/Stock Montage

Squanto adopted the English as his family. About the time that the *Mayflower* sailed back to England in early spring of 1621, Squanto showed the Pilgrims the best fishing spots. Squanto also taught them how to plant corn and how to use dead fish to fertilize the ground.

One day when the corn was still being planted, Governor Carver came home from the fields complaining of a headache. He lay down, fell into a coma, and died several days later. William Bradford was then chosen as governor. Under Bradford's direction the Pilgrims continued to build. By the end of the summer of 1621 Plymouth was a town with streets, houses, and several public buildings.

At harvest time, the Pilgrims found that the seeds they had brought from England for such crops as wheat and peas had done poorly. However, the corn grown under Squanto's supervision was beautiful. Massachusetts was a paradise to the Pilgrims in that autumn of 1621. Hunters bagged deer, ducks, and turkeys. The colonists gathered wild grapes, which they made into a sweet drink. In addition, a supply of cod and bass was left from the summer's fishing trips. The Pilgrims were so happy about all this abundance that they decided to have a thanksgiving celebration.

The first Thanksgiving.

Historical Pictures/Stock Montage

Governor Bradford invited Massasoit and about ninety of his fellow Native Americans to the three-day celebration, held sometime in the fall of 1621. The Wampanoags brought deer meat and wild turkeys to the feast, while the colonists provided fish, geese, ducks, corn bread, and succotash (corn and beans cooked together). This was the first thanksgiving feast held by the English in what is now the United States. Later, the Pilgrims continued to hold thanksgiving celebrations in years of good harvests. This tradition grew into the Thanksgiving holiday now held across the United States on the fourth Thursday of every November.

THE EARLY HOUSES

from THE PILGRIMS OF PLYMOUTH
by Barbara L. Beck

A reconstruction of early Plymouth houses.

Plimoth Plantation, Plymouth, Massachusetts

The first homes built by the Pilgrims had only one room, with an overhead loft for sleeping. Felling trees and sawing them into planks was no easy task, especially since these houses were built in cold weather and the lumber had to be hauled a quarter of a mile to the settlement. The roofs were thatched with rushes, and the chimneys were made of sticks of wood daubed with clay. The tiny windows were covered with oilpaper and were heavily draped with cloth to keep out the cold.

Each house had a large fireplace, in front of which everyone gathered for warmth, food, and light. Cranes were used to hold large brass and iron cooking pots and kettles over the wood fire. A huge table, a stool or two, some plain wooden chairs, a chest, and beds took up most of the space in the tiny house. At bedtime, the children went up the ladder to the sleeping loft.

Naturally there was a lot of clutter. The table might hold a freshly killed duck, some herbs from the garden, a basket of wild berries, the Bible and perhaps another book, a loaf of bread fresh from an outdoor oven, bowls, and a gun in need of repair. The walls had many pegs on which clothing was hung. Stored in other parts of the room might be a barrel of beer, a musket, a fowling piece for shooting wild birds, a keg of gunpowder, a bag of feathers for stuffing a mattress or pillow, a whisk broom, a small chest for clothing and linens, woodcutting tools, and many other things.

It was not long before the colonists found their quarters too cramped, and by 1640 many new and larger homes had

The fireplace in this early home was used for both heating the
room and cooking the meals.

been constructed. These houses were built around central brick chimneys and had wooden roofs; thatched roofs were no longer used because of the risk of fire. In addition to a kitchen, the new houses had a parlor, which was often used as a bedroom. Upstairs were two more bedrooms with fireplaces.

In some families the most prized belonging was a huge homemade fourposter bed. A big bag stuffed with feathers often served as a mattress. Less well-to-do folk stuffed their mattresses with bits of cloth, while the really poor people slept on corn husks. Mattress springs were made of cords laced across the bed; they were always getting loose and sagging. Underneath the bed was a truckle, or trundle, bed—a small bed that was stored under the bigger bed in the daytime and pulled out at night. Cribs, cradles, and cots were put anywhere there was room. There were plenty of blankets for warmth.

The wide pine-board floors were scoured with beach sand to keep them clean. By the 1640s, most of the oil-paper windows had been replaced by diamond-paned casements that still did not let in much light. Both outside and inside, the walls were made of cedar. Unpainted cedar clapboards were often put up only on the front of a house for the benefit of passersby. The Pilgrim houses were not log cabins. The log cabin was introduced to America in the 1640s by Delaware Bay settlers from Sweden.

Many houses also had attached lean-tos. These supplied space for additional bedrooms or perhaps for a study.

JOLIET AND MARQUETTE DISCOVER THE MISSISSIPPI

from THE JESUIT RELATIONS AND
ALLIED DOCUMENTS
*illustrated by Mary Beth Schwark
and Bob Kuester*

*In 1673, Joliet and Marquette explored the Mississippi River
for France. They found Native American villages along the
shores of this "great river." The French thought of the Native
Americans as "savages" because they lived differently and did
not have the same religious beliefs. A French order of
Catholic priests wanted to record everything about this New
World and kept detailed diaries of the expeditions. In this
excerpt, Joliet and Marquette explain their journey to a group
of Jesuit priests, who record their findings.*

There are forests on both sides, as far as the sea. The
most vigorous trees that one sees there are a species
of cotton-tree, of extraordinary girth and height.
The savages therefore use these trees for making canoes—
all of one piece, fifty feet in length and three in width, in

which thirty men with all their baggage can embark. They make them of much more graceful shape than we do ours. They have so great a number of them that in a single village one sees as many as 280 together.

The nations are located near the Great River, or farther inland. Our travelers counted more than 40 villages, most of which consisted of 60 to 80 cabins. Some villages even contained 300 cabins, such as that of the Illinois, which contains over 8,000 souls. All of the savages who compose it seem to have a gentle nature; they are affable and obliging. Our Frenchmen experienced the effects of this civility at the first village that they entered, for there a present was made them—a pipe-stem for smoking, about three feet long, adorned with feathers of various kinds. This gift has almost a religious meaning among these peoples; because the calumet is, as it were, a passport and safeguard to enable one to go in safety everywhere, no one daring to injure in any manner those who bear this caduceus [wooden staff]. It has only to be displayed, and life is secure, even

MINNESOTA

WISCONSIN

MICHIGAN

IOWA

ILLINOIS

OHIO

INDIANA

MISSISSIPPI RIVER

MISSOURI

KENTUCKY

TENNESSEE

ARKANSAS RIVER

ARKANSAS

MISS.

AL.

GA.

in the thickest of the fight. As there is a peace-pipe, so also is there a war-pipe; these differ, however, solely in the color of the feathers that cover them—red being the token of war, while the other colors are signs of peace. Many things might indeed be said about this pipe-stem, as well as of the manners and customs of those peoples. Until such time as we receive the relation thereof, we shall merely say that the women are very modest; also, that, when they do wrong, their noses are cut off. It is they who, with the old men, have the care of tilling the soil; and, when the seed is sown, all go together to hunt the wild cattle, which supply them with food. From the hides of these, they make their garments, dressing the skin with a certain kind of earth, which also serves them as a dye.

The soil is so fertile that it yields corn three times a year. It produces, naturally, fruits which are unknown to us and are excellent. Grapes, plums, apples, mulberries, chestnuts, pomegranates, and many others are gathered everywhere, and almost at all times, for winter is only known there by the rains.

The country is equally divided into prairies and forests, and provides fine pastures for the great number of animals with which it abounds. The wild cattle never flee. The Father counted as many as 400 of them in a single herd. Stags, does, and deer are almost everywhere. Turkeys strut about, on all sides. Parroquets fly in flocks of 10 to 12; and quail rise on the prairies at every moment.

Through the midst of this fine country our travelers passed, advancing upon the Great River.

JUDITH:
THE LIFE OF A SLAVE
Cathleene Hellier and
Brandon Miller
illustrated by Mary C. Gilman

She was known simply as Judith, and what she felt or thought about her life as a slave in eighteenth-century Williamsburg, we will never know. Slaves made up half of Williamsburg's population, but none left a written record of their feelings about slavery.

Many families in Williamsburg owned slaves, but most owned only one or two. Wealthier families might have owned ten to fifteen slaves but seldom more than twenty. Slaves were an important part of the daily life and business of the Virginia capital, although they were often over-looked by historians because they left no written record.

Most slaves in Williamsburg worked as domestic servants or were trained as craftsmen. Many domestic slaves per-formed several tasks, including nursing, ironing, spinning, gardening, and sewing. Slaves who worked as craftsmen included carpenters, blacksmiths, shoemakers, and cabinet-makers, among others.

From what we can gather, Judith was William Prentis's family cook. As cook, her workdays were long and demanding. The kitchen where she worked was separate from the house, and the open fire made it very hot during the long Virginia summers. Judith rose early to prepare the fire and to cook the Prentis family's breakfast. As soon as breakfast was cleared away, she began the preparations for dinner, the largest meal of the day, served early in the afternoon. Dinner in a household like the Prentis's might have included two courses, including several kinds of meat, vegetables, relishes, beverages, and desserts. Judith also cleaned the many pots, spits, and kettles required to make such a meal. Happily for her, the leftovers from dinner were served for supper in the early evening.

Judith had little spare time to spend with her family. Because she was the cook, however, her children often received special treats that their mother saved from the Prentis's table. Her older daughters probably helped her in the kitchen on occasion.

Judith and her children lived above the kitchen, under the eaves. They slept and kept their few possessions there. The slave owners supplied their domestic slaves with simple clothing and bedding. Sometimes the slaves even wore hand-me-downs from the master's family. Domestic slaves often received tips from guests, and some slaves earned money by raising chickens for sale. They could spend this money in the local stores, buying better clothing for special occasions or items to make their living quarters more comfortable.

Some slave children, including Judith's daughter Molly, went to special schools for blacks, an unusual opportunity for slaves in Colonial Virginia. One school, the Bray School, was founded by an English philanthropic (charitable) organization that listed Benjamin Franklin as a member. The school in Williamsburg opened in 1760. Students were taught to read the Bible, keep themselves clean and behave well, and speak distinctly. The founders hoped that pupils would attend the school for three years, but this rarely happened. When children were old enough to work, they were usually taken out of school.

Like slaves everywhere, Judith lived under a strict legal code designed to prevent slave uprisings. Blacks could not possess weapons or assemble except for public worship. (Church teaching enforced the idea that it was their duty to be obedient and patient.) Punishments for stealing or for resisting a white man included whipping, mutilation, and hanging. Yet slaves who committed a crime in which a person was not killed usually received a light sentence if it was their first offense. Even though laws were strict, they were not always strictly enforced. For example, some masters allowed their slaves to have guns for hunting.

Runaway slaves were returned to their masters. Runaways were often trying to visit family members who lived in other parts of the colony. Some ran away because they were trying to escape a particular master. The busy capital was a favorite hide-out for runaways, and it seems that Williamsburg slaves did a fairly good job of hiding fugitives.

The family life of a slave was uncertain. If a master died or got into debt, some or all of his slaves might be sold. Sometimes the members of slave families were sold to different masters who lived far apart. Slaves must have feared these separations. When William Prentis died in 1765, he willed Judith and her three children to his teen-age daughter Elizabeth. When Elizabeth died unmarried in 1770, Judith and her children passed to Elizabeth's older brother John. By then, Judith had at least five children. John also inherited the family home in Williamsburg, and Judith and her children continued to live on the property.

During each of these upheavals in the Prentis family, Judith probably worried about the fate of her own family.

Yet she had more cause to worry when John Prentis became very sick in 1775. John's wife was mentally ill and would not be able to manage the household if her husband died. When he did die, Judith was alarmed to learn that he had bequeathed only three of her children to his brother Joseph. Another daughter, Molly, was to be kept by John's family but hired out to work for others. Her work would provide money to help support John's widow. Finally, Judith learned that because the widow could not run a household, Judith would no longer be needed. She and her youngest son, Tom, were to be sold at auction. Her worst fears had come true; she and her children would be separated.

The slaves of Colonial Williamsburg had a big impact on the city's life. These men and women worked in almost every household, in the taverns, at the college, and in the craft shops. Overall, Williamsburg slaves were a trained and skilled group. Some even had a little education. But what a Williamsburg slave actually felt, feared, or hoped for, we can only imagine.

FREEDOM

Langston Hughes
illustrated by Tyrone Geter

Freedom will not come
Today, this year
      Nor ever
Through compromise and fear.

I have as much right
As the other fellow has
      To stand
On my two feet
And own the land.

I tire so of hearing people say,
Let things take their course.
Tomorrow is another day.
I do not need my freedom when I'm dead.
I cannot live on tomorrow's bread.
      Freedom
      Is a strong seed
      Planted
      In a great need.
      I live here, too.
      I want freedom
      Just as you.

MEET LANGSTON HUGHES, POET

Langston Hughes grew up in Kansas, Illinois, and Ohio. As a
young man, he traveled to Africa and Europe, gaining experiences
that he would later write about. By the time he finished college,
Hughes had already won awards for his writing ability.
He wrote poetry, newspaper columns, novels, short stories, plays,
a musical, and stories for children. Hughes's main interest was in
recording the history and artistic contributions of African Americans.
In his writings, he explained their problems and also the ways in which they
influenced America's culture. Although Langston Hughes wrote many things, he is
best known for his poetry. The Dream Keeper and Other Poems and
Black Misery were written especially for children.

❧ 261 ❧

Should you, my lord, while you peruse my song,
Wonder from whence my love of Freedom sprung,
Whence flow these wishes for the common good,
By feeling hearts alone best understood,
I, young in life, by seeming cruel fate
Was snatch'd from Afric's fancy'd happy seat.

PHILLIS WHEATLEY

POET

Susan Altman
illustrated by Marcy Ramsey

Those are the words of Phillis Wheatley, a young, African-born woman who was kidnapped by slave traders when she was about eight years old and brought to Boston, Massachusetts, in 1761. There she was bought by John Wheatley, a wealthy merchant tailor, as a lady's maid for his wife Susannah.

A small, frail child, Phillis was well cared for. She was assigned chores that she was able to do. Very intelligent, she learned English quickly and was taught to read. When she was fourteen, she began writing poetry. Her first work to receive widespread attention was "An Elegiac Poem, on the Death of that Celebrated Divine . . . George Whitefield." It was printed in Boston in 1770.

Phillis Wheatley was never very strong. When her health began to fail in 1772, the Wheatleys freed her and sent her to England. While she was there, she impressed several members of the nobility. They arranged for her book, *Poems on Various Subjects, Religious and Moral*, to be published. Many prominent Massachusetts men (including John Hancock) signed the foreword of her book.

Arrangements were made for Ms. Wheatley to be introduced to the king and queen of England. But before the meeting could take place, she received word that Mrs. Wheatley was ill, so she quickly returned to America.

When Mrs. Wheatley died in 1774, Ms. Wheatley remained with the family and kept house for John Wheatley. She continued to write, and, in 1775, dedicated a poem to George Washington, which appeared in Thomas Paine's *Pennsylvania Magazine*. Washington was so impressed that he invited her to visit him at his headquarters in Cambridge, Massachusetts.

After the death of John Wheatley in 1778, Ms. Wheatley was forced to move from the house where she had grown up. Shortly thereafter, she married a man named John Peters. He was frequently away, and the marriage was unhappy. Although in ill health, Phillis Wheatley had to work as a servant to support herself.

Two of her three children died shortly after they were born. Then on December 5, 1784, she passed away at age thirty-one. Her third child died the same day.

Phillis Wheatley is remembered today because of her role in the development of black American literature. Her sensitive poetry proved at the time that blacks, when given the opportunity, were equal to whites, both intellectually and emotionally. At a time when the fight against slavery often seemed endless, Phillis Wheatley's poems provided both hope and ammunition.

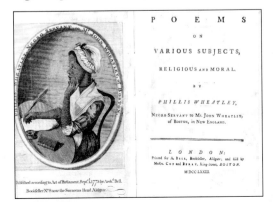

Title page of Phillis Wheatley's book, published in 1773.

Library of Congress/PHOTRI

PAUL CUFFE
Karen Sapp

Paul Cuffe's silhouette, appearing on his business
seal, was the only picture made of him.

Many people believe that the first Africans in America were brought to the colonies in chains and remained slaves their whole lives. The first African colonists, however, were not slaves at all; they were indentured servants. They were brought to America from Africa to work without pay for a period of time—usually four to seven years—in exchange for food, shelter, and clothing. After serving the period of indenture, the person was free. There were many indentured servants in the colonies. Some were African, many were European. Over time, more workers were needed in the colonies. Because there were not enough European and Native American workers, the colonists began the practice of slavery. In 1770, there were nearly 700,000 slaves in the 13 colonies. Free Africans also continued to increase in population, and in 1790, close to 60,000 free African colonists were counted.

The status of free African Americans was never really clear. They were not slaves, yet they were not treated as equal to white colonists. Strange as it may seem, free African Americans were allowed to have slaves, as long as they were not white slaves. Those who owned property were required to pay taxes, but were not permitted to vote.

The growth of the colonies created new opportunities for all colonists. Some free African Americans were able to open shops or businesses of their own. Paul Cuffe was one of these. He not only prospered as a businessman in the shipping industry, but was active in fighting for the rights of free African colonists and slaves.

Paul was born in Westport, Massachusetts, to free parents in 1759. He was the youngest of ten children. His father, Cuffe Slocum, had been a member of the Ashanti tribe in West Africa before he was captured by slave traders and brought to America. Cuffe was sold to the Slocum family in Massachusetts. After serving them for fifteen years, he was told he could

This bill of sale for Cuffe Slocum,
Paul's father, documents when he was sold into
slavery in 1742.

New Bedford Free Public Library

buy his freedom by doing extra work. Within three years, Cuffe became a free man, at which time he married Ruth Moses, a Native American. Ruth's family members were descendants of the Wampanoag tribe. This was the tribe that helped the Pilgrims survive their first winter in America. Cuffe farmed and fished for a living. He later started his own carpentry business.

The close-knit family of Cuffe Slocum was proud of its heritage. As the children grew, each shared in the responsibilities of the family farm, fishing, and carpentry businesses. In 1772, Paul's father died. To honor his father, Paul changed his name from Paul Cuffe Slocum to Paul Cuffe, dropping his father's slave name. A year later, at the age of fourteen, Paul left home to begin a career at sea. As a cargo ship crew member, Paul sailed to the West Indies, where he witnessed for the first time the horrors of the slave system.

Cuffe saw the horrors of the slave trade when he visited the West Indies. Here, ships were filled with slaves from Africa.

The Bettmann Archive

Millions of Africans who worked in the fields of huge sugar plantations were beaten, whipped, and even branded. With no medical care, many of these slaves died. It was at this time that Paul began thinking about how this brutal system could be stopped.

In 1779, at twenty years of age, Paul and his brother David built a boat and went into business for themselves. Although it was right in the middle of the Revolutionary War, it was a good time to attempt such a venture. British raids had destroyed many of the colony's big fleets, so small traders had a chance to compete. Following an encounter with pirates off the New England coast, David chose to seek out a less risky business. But Paul, happy with his independence, continued to make the dangerous voyages.

Attacks from pirates off the Massachusetts coast were always a threat to ship crews.
New York Public Library

Although Paul's shipping business thrived, it did encounter trouble from an unexpected source. The Commonwealth of Massachusetts demanded a large sum in taxes even though Paul Cuffe, as an African colonist, was not allowed to vote. While his fellow colonists were fighting a war of independence from England's government because it forced them to pay taxes without allowing them political representation, Paul Cuffe was being denied the same privilege.

He could not stand for such injustice. Paul and his brother John Cuffe, and five other free African colonists petitioned the county council. They did not feel they should have to pay the tax unless they were allowed to vote. The Cuffe case received much public attention. The council members finally agreed to accept only a small tax payment from the men, a partial victory.

By 1783, slavery was outlawed in Massachusetts. Tax-paying, free African male property owners were finally granted the right to vote. That same year, Paul married Alice Pequit, a woman of Wampanoag descent. Conditions were beginning to improve for free African colonists. A decade later, when Paul was thirty-five, his business had grown to include an entire fleet of ships. He continued to put his efforts and his fortune to work to improve the

Cuffe owned schooners like the one below.

The *Fame* of Salem, topsail schooner. 1800. William Ward. Watercolor. The Peabody Museum of Salem.

conditions of other colonial Africans. For instance, when he found there was no school for African children in his area, he hired a teacher and built one himself.

Although it was a long, hard process, Paul realized that he could indeed bring about changes in society. Still, obstacles continued to discourage him, causing Paul to think that maybe the only way for African Americans to rise to their potential would be to establish their own colony back in Africa. Paul made two trips to the West African colony of Sierra Leone. Here he hoped to have African settlers from America set up a trading center and build new industries. Sadly, Paul became ill and died in 1817 before he could realize his dream. But his accomplishments survived him, providing an example to all people that justice can be won with courage and persistence.

Cuffe dreamed of starting a new colony for blacks in Sierra Leone, Africa.

LIFE IN PHILADELPHIA

from THE PENNSYLVANIA COLONY
by Dennis B. Fradin

I n the year 1750, Philadelphia was Pennsylvania's largest
city. Of the 120,000 colonists in Pennsylvania, about
15,000 of them lived in Philadelphia. Only Boston,
Massachusetts, with 20,000 people, had a larger population
than Philadelphia.

As the largest city in Pennsylvania, Philadelphia was an important
cultural and trade center.
The Historical Society of Pennsylvania

Because William Penn and his fellow Quakers founded it, Philadelphia was called the *Quaker City*. But by 1750, it was home to only eight hundred Quaker families, comprising about a fourth of the population. Philadelphia was also home to large numbers of German and Scotch-Irish people, and to people of many other nationalities.

The clay along the river banks was good for making bricks, and by 1750 Philadelphia was known for its red brick buildings. Wealthy Philadelphians lived in brick mansions, but most people lived in small brick houses.

A great deal of street paving had taken place since the 1740s, but by 1750, many Philadelphians still complained about the remaining unpaved streets that had tree stumps and mud puddles. And because people piled up their garbage

on them, many of Philadelphia's streets were filthy. In 1750, Mayor Thomas Lawrence ordered all families to keep the areas in front of their homes clean, but few people paid attention to the new law.

In 1751, the city installed whale-oil lamps on its main streets. At first, the new lamps were constantly smudged by smoke, but jack-of-all-trades Ben Franklin solved that problem by changing their design slightly. Then the main problem was young people breaking the lamps by hurling apples and rocks at them.

The Philadelphians of the early 1750s worked at a variety of jobs. Boston was the only colonial city that did more shipping than Philadelphia, and hundreds of Philadelphians worked at shipping-related jobs. Workers built sailing vessels in the city's shipyards. Merchants earned fortunes buying and selling goods that went in and out of the city. Dock workers earned their living by unloading the ships that came up the Delaware River to Philadelphia, then loading them with new cargo.

Philadelphians also worked as blacksmiths, tailors, carriage-makers, glass-makers, teachers, ministers, printers, booksellers, and lawyers. Hundreds worked in the city's more than one hundred taverns and inns.

Instead of working far from home as many people do today, the Philadelphians of the 1750s commonly had their shops and homes in the same building. Because many people could not read, some businesses had picture signs showing their names. For example, outside a metalworker's

Colonial school in Pennsylvania.
The Bettmann Archive

shop called the Golden Cup there was a picture of a golden cup. That way even people who could not read could find the shop.

The reason why so many people could not read was that Pennsylvania had no public-school system. There were a few church-run and private schools, and in the early 1750s several Philadelphians set up free schools for the poor, but free public education did not get going until the mid-1800s. Until then, many people received little or no schooling.

Wealthy families hired private tutors to teach their young sons Latin, Greek, and other advanced subjects. When they became teenagers, some of the young men (but not the women) attended college in Europe or in other colonies. Pennsylvania's first college did not get its start until 1751, when the Philadelphia Academy opened. Ben Franklin was a founder of this school, which today is the University of Pennsylvania.

Printing press owned
by Ben Franklin.

Printing and publishing were very important in Philadelphia in the 1750s. The city had two main newspapers at the time—the *Pennsylvania Gazette* and the *Pennsylvania Journal*. Philadelphians sat in the city's taverns, inns, and parks passing the newspapers from person to person. Often someone would read the newspaper aloud so that people who didn't know how to read could learn about the news.

Like today, the front pages of the Philadelphia newspapers often related news from far away places like England, Italy, France, Russia, and Spain. But the stories weren't reported until several months had passed because it took that long to send the news by ship across the ocean. For example, the February 13, 1750, *Gazette* reported an event that had occurred in Moscow, Russia, on October 15 of the previous year! News stories from the other twelve colonies often took a few weeks before they were published in the Philadelphia papers.

The old newspapers reveal that the Philadelphians of the 1750s had many of the same interests as people today. There were many stories on local politics and events. The papers contained numerous advertisements from store owners who wanted to sell their wares and from shipowners who wanted people to use their vessels. Lotteries were so popular that the winning numbers were sometimes printed in the paper. One aspect of the newspapers that makes them seem very old is the large number of rewards offered for the return of runaway slaves and indentured servants.

The most famous printer in Philadelphia at the time was Benjamin Franklin, publisher of the *Pennsylvania Gazette* and the extremely popular *Poor Richard's Almanack*. Each year a number of Philadelphia publishers came out with almanacs—booklets that told about the movements of heavenly bodies, gave weather forecasts, and offered little sayings. *Poor Richard's Almanack*, published by Franklin from 1733 to 1758, was the second-most popular book in colonial America—behind only the Bible.

Franklin wrote his almanac under the name Richard Saunders, who was supposed to be "Poor Richard." The sayings in his almanac became household expressions around Philadelphia and later around the whole country. Parents

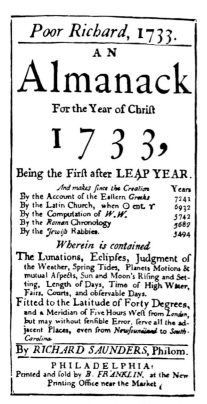

Left: Poor Richard's Almanack, 1733; *below:* sayings from the *Almanack*. Have you heard either of these sayings before?

The Bettmann Archive

Franklin at age twenty.

who wanted their children to go to sleep would say, "As Poor Richard says, *Early to bed and early to rise, makes a man healthy, wealthy, and wise,*" which came from the 1735 almanac. To describe a long-winded minister, people might say, "As Poor Richard says, *A good example is the best sermon,*" which came from the 1747 almanac.

The thousands of people who eagerly awaited Franklin's 1750 almanac were not disappointed. That year his witty sayings included "Genius without education is like silver in the mine" and "Little strokes fell great oaks." Poor Richard especially liked to tell people how to make and keep money, and in the 1751 almanac he came up with the saying "Time is money."

In addition to his publishing ventures, Ben Franklin was famous for improving the city in many ways. In 1731, he had founded the Library Company of Philadelphia, the colonies' first library to circulate books. Five years later he had founded the thirteen colonies' first volunteer fire department. In 1751, the year the academy opened, Franklin helped start the Pennsylvania Hospital, the country's first general hospital. People wondered how Ben Franklin could do so much around the city and still find time for his electrical experiments and a growing political career in the Pennsylvania Assembly.

Philadelphia in the mid-1700s was in the process of growing from a small town into a real city. Many new buildings were going up, and even the State House was being improved. From 1750 to 1753 Philadelphians watched as a tower was built on the State House. In 1751, the Pennsylvania Assembly decided that a bell should be placed in the new tower to celebrate the fiftieth anniversary of William Penn's Charter of Privileges. An order for a one ton bell was placed with a foundry in England. Because William Penn had planned his colony as a place of liberty, the Biblical words PROCLAIM LIBERTY THROUGHOUT ALL THE LAND UNTO ALL THE INHABITANTS THEREOF were to be inscribed on the bell.

The ship carrying the bell arrived in Philadelphia in August of 1752. The tower was not yet finished, so the bell was taken to the State House yard for testing. As soon as it was rung, however, the bell cracked. Two ironworkers recast the huge bell, which was placed in the tower in 1753.

As they watched it being raised to the State House tower, the Philadelphians of 1753 would have been surprised to know that the bell would one day become a symbol of America, and that it would even appear on some of the nation's coins. After being rung at many historic occasions, including the adoption of the Declaration of Independence, it became known as the Liberty Bell. And because the Declaration of Independence was adopted there, the State House became known as Independence Hall.

FINE ART
COLONIAL LIFE

Cornhusk dolls. c. 1900. Seneca,
Cattaraugus Reservation, New York.

National Museum of the American Indian,
Smithsonian Institution. 3486

Battle of Bunker's Hill. 1786.
John Trumbull.

Oil on canvas. Yale University Art Gallery,
New Haven, Connecticut

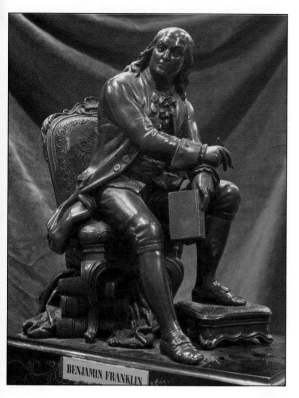

Benjamin Franklin at his writing table.
c. 1778. Artist unknown.

Bronze. Musée de l'Amitié Franco-Americaine,
Blerancourt, France. Photo: © Erich Lessing/Art Resource

St. Tammany weathervane from East Branch,
New York. c. 1850. Artist unknown.

Molded paper and painted copper, 102" x 103" x 12".
Collection of the Museum of American Folk Art, New York,
Museum of American Folk Art Purchase. 1963.2.1

Early American quilt showing village
and church. c. 1800–1820. Sarah Furman Warner.

Appliqué. Henry Ford Museum and Greenfield Village,
Dearborn, Michigan

THE
FIGHTING
GROUND

Avi

illustrated by Stephen Marchesi

Jonathan is thirteen years old and lives on a farm near
Trenton, New Jersey, during the Revolutionary War. For the
past three years, he has longed to be a soldier in the
Continental Army. The colonists are fighting England to gain
their independence. They want to form their own government
and make their own laws. Jonathan's father, who has already
served in the war and been wounded, does not want his
young son to join in the fighting.

It is April 7, 1779. A bell has rung, warning citizens in that
area that enemy troops are approaching. Without telling his
father, Jonathan joins a group of volunteers, led by a corporal
in the Continental Army. The group of volunteers finds a
position near Rockton to sit and wait for the British forces.
A distant drumming sound tells them the enemy is near.

2:30

Nobody moved. They just stood there, listening to the drum. It came loud and regular, like an angry clock. Then slyly, the fife music slid into a playful tune, poking, plucking at their brittle senses. A tightness ran up and down Jonathan's spine, into the nape of his neck. He tried to cough, only to realize he had been holding his breath.

He looked about. The men were all staring. What they were seeing he couldn't tell. One man pressed an open hand to his jaw, drawing his fingers across, pulling at his lips, making them grotesque. Another man kept licking his lips.

The Corporal listened with great intensity, as if the sound of fife and drum brought a special message to his ears.

"Line! Line!" he suddenly shouted, springing to life. "Line here! Seven in front! The short ones! The rest in back! The taller. Gentlemen, hurry!"

The men began to run forward and back in a frenzy. Jonathan, not understanding where he should stand, stood in place where he was until he felt a hard slap against his back.

"Move!" came the angry command.

Mechanically, he turned toward the Corporal who, reaching out, took hold of his shoulder and shoved him forward, then spun him into position. "Front line!" he ordered. "Front line!"

Jonathan stayed where he had been put.

But other men came forward. There was more pushing, more shoving. The Corporal, holding to his horse's
bridle, tried to keep the beast calm, all the while shouting
directions.

"Here, here! No, fool, there! Take your place! There!
No, there. Two paces back! Dress your lines! Not right
behind! Dress them, you fools! Gentlemen, your lines!"

Jonathan found himself moved this way and that, one
step this direction, two the other. People stepped on his
feet. The Corporal attempted to mount his horse, only to
slip and fall to the ground. The men gawked, but made no

move to help. The Corporal sprang up on his own. This
time he climbed up successfully. Holding a pistol in one
hand, he wheeled his horse about in a useless circle.

Jonathan could hear the breathing of the men all about,
quick and agitated. Beyond that, he heard the tap-tapping
of the drum, the nagging, relentless curl of the fife.

"There!" cried the Corporal. "That's it. Now, gentlemen,
load your guns, for goodness' sake. Load your guns!"

All around came thudding as guns dropped to the
ground, stocks to earth, followed by the pop of snaps, as
leather cartridge pouches opened.

"You, boy!" came a cry. "Do your loading! Are you daft! Load your gun!"

2:35

Hurriedly, Jonathan lowered his gun to the ground. With one hand he held the muzzle, with the other he tried to open the cartridge pouch. The fastening would not give. He placed the gun on the ground before his feet.

"Pick that up, you idiot!" came a shout into his ear.

In a panic, Jonathan reached down and snatched up his gun. Resting it in the crook of his arm and clumsily using both hands, he yanked his cartridge pouch open. The wooden catch broke. His fingers, trembling, touched the cartridges. He pulled one up. It was made of rough, brown paper twisted into a tube, one end further twisted tight like a candle wick. The small package contained a measure of gunpowder and one lead ball.

Putting the twisted paper to his mouth, Jonathan tore at it with his teeth. It did not give. He tugged harder. This time the paper tore—too much. He could taste powder on his tongue. He spat it out.

Hands shaking, he tried to maneuver the gun upright while still holding the torn cartridge so it wouldn't spill. But the barrel was too high. He had to stand on his toes to pour the powder in. Then, crumpling the paper in his fist, he wadded it around the lead ball, poking both into the barrel mouth.

Unsteadily, Jonathan yanked out the ramrod from beneath the gun barrel, where it was lodged. He reached high, higher, trying to stick the swinging rod into the barrel so as to set the ball snug proper. Just managing to get the rod in, he waited for it to slide down. It would not drop. He had to reach high again, stretching on his toes as far as he could, pushing on the rod and pressing it against the wadded ball but not pressing too hard, lest he crush the powder grains and make the gun misfire.

Jonathan pulled out the rod and let it drop to the ground, only to remember that that was wrong. He bent over to pick it up, pointing the gun barrel down. To his horror the lead ball rolled out of the gun mouth onto the ground. Frantic, he snatched it up, hoping no one had seen what had happened. He flipped the ball back down into the gun.

Again he bent over, this time making sure the gun kept pointing up. The ball stayed in. Grabbing the rod, he shoved it into the muzzle once more, pressing the load tightly. Then he pulled the rod out and placed it correctly in its socket.

Holding the loaded gun before him, pointing it waveringly forward and up, he reached for his powder horn and brought it around. With his teeth, he edged off the cap. Trying not to put in too much or too little, he trickled fine firing grains into the priming pan beneath the hammer lock and flint.

That done, he pushed the cap back on the horn and let it drop. Then he brought the gun upright with both hands.

He was ready at last.

2:40

Sweating all over, hoping no one had seen his clumsy slowness, Jonathan glanced about. No one was looking at him. Guns ready, faces rigid, the men were staring down the road. Even as he watched, Jonathan saw one of the men stick out his tongue, lick his lips, then hastily wipe away the spittle. Another man kept clearing his throat. A third rubbed an irritated eye.

Only then did Jonathan realize how much closer was the sound of fife and drum. He snapped his head about. At the end of the road, as it came out from behind the tall trees, soldiers were advancing.

2:41

Jonathan watched, spellbound, as the troops marched into view. Three by three they came, ten rows, thirty soldiers, all moving in lockstep, their legs lifting high and stiff.

Though still at the bottom of the hill, the soldiers seemed enormous. Never had he seen such men. Giants.

In the growing gloom of the darkening clouds their golden, pointed caps glowed brightly. Many wore great mustaches. Their jackets were blue with red cuffs and bright white buttons, their vests dark yellow. Their trousers, striped in red and white, met boots of crow-feather black.

Each had a bayonet at his waist, a crossed white sash around his chest. And in his left hand each carried a tall flintlock gun.

"*Hessians*," the man next to Jonathan said. "*Hessians*." The words filled the air with a dreadful weight.

2:43

Jonathan felt the men around him shift uneasily, sensing the fear that had settled over the group like a suffocating blanket.

Hessians.

"So many of them . . ." came a strained voice from right behind.

Hessians. The mercenaries who killed for coin . . .

"Shut up!" roared the Corporal, trying to keep his voice under control. "No talking. Stand your ground!"

"Them's grenadiers," came another voice, unnaturally high. "See how big they are? Their match cases? See them? Do you see that boys? Grenadiers."

As Jonathan watched, the enemy troops continued to pace themselves to the beat of the drum. He couldn't see the drummer or the player, but he knew they must be boys. Perhaps, he thought, they were younger than he. He wanted to see them, wanted them to be much younger.

The Hessians continued to march.

"Keep your lines!" the Corporal shouted. "Keep them!"

The men lifted their guns and pointed them straight down the road at the oncoming soldiers.

"Hold your fire till I tell you!" the Corporal shouted. "Don't waste your shot. They're still too far!"

Jonathan could not take his eyes from the advancing troops. All of them had cleared the bend now, moving so steadily that Jonathan wondered if they saw that the road was blocked. But just as he had the thought, they came to a stop, and the smooth flow of their march broke with a clumsiness that momentarily eased Jonathan's tension.

On his horse, the Hessian officer cantered forward, looking up the hill at the Americans.

Jonathan hefted his gun a little higher. He glanced behind. His father's friend, his head glistening with sweat, was there.

"Aim low!" the Corporal cried. "Or your shot'll go high!"

Jonathan looked at his own gun. At the moment it felt light. He stole a look at the men around him. He saw their fingers flex, grip, release, and grip again.

"Where's your Snydertown Committee, Corporal?" came a call. "Why don't they come? Is there something we don't know?"

The Corporal, never taking his eyes from the Hessians, and keeping his back to his own men, said nothing. His horse, blowing out its breath, shifted nervously.

Jonathan's mouth felt hard and dry, his tongue thick. A bad taste was in his mouth. Whom could he ask for a drink? Who wouldn't mind? He gazed about, trying to pick someone, thinking only that he was more thirsty than he had ever been in his life. But the men were all too fixed upon the road for him to ask. He did not dare to speak.

Down the road the Hessians remained standing still. Only the officer on the horse was moving. Jonathan heard the sharp clop of its hooves. The officer's large mustache was turned up at either end. He carried no gun, but there was a sword in his hand that flashed in the steel-gray light. He kept looking up the hill, craning his neck now this way, now that.

Jonathan suddenly realized that he had never seen an enemy soldier before. He had seen Tories, but they were only Americans. What he was seeing right before him were real enemies.

Down the road the Hessian officer waved his sword and shouted something to his men. The drum began to beat again. The fife played high, reedy notes. From behind Jonathan felt the wind cold against his neck. The gun, swaying, felt heavy.

"Spread out a bit," the Corporal ordered. "Don't give so much target."

Everyone shifted.

"When I give the call," he continued, "the first line fires. Then the second moves on forward. You on the first line, you step back and load again. You get that? Two rounds a minute, boys, two!"

Jonathan's heart sank. *Two rounds a minute.* He couldn't do it. He wished he'd practiced more.

The tramp of the soldiers cut through his regrets. Jonathan turned. The Hessians, their red-and-white legs moving in high-stepping, winking unison, had begun once more to advance. Their guns rose beside their golden caps.

The sight made Jonathan dizzy. He swayed. The gun felt heavier.

"You are ready?" he heard close to his ear. Jonathan turned. It was the Frenchman. He was standing next to him.

Jonathan tried to answer, but found he had no voice. He nodded.

"They are the big ones, certainly," said the Frenchman.

"Steady boys, keep steady!" the Corporal called, moving off to one side. "Remember, there's a storm coming. If it rains, keep your pans covered and dry. Wait till we've got fifty yards between us, boys, fifty yards or less, fifty yards or less!"

How far, Jonathan wondered, was fifty yards? How many feet was that? What spot would that be on the road? Would anyone tell him? Why didn't anyone tell him anything? Don't they know, he said to himself, that I'm the youngest here?

His heart beat with every stroke of the drum; the soldiers advanced to the self-same sound. If his heart stopped beating, Jonathan wondered, would they stop too?

Watching, he couldn't believe how they came together, shoulder to shoulder, no one moving out of step, their legs lifting stiffly, perfectly.

The Hessian officer shouted something.

"What did he say?" asked one of the Americans.

"Don't know."

"What's he saying?"

"Ready!" cried the Corporal.

Feeling the backs of his legs grow tight, Jonathan pulled his gun up. He tried to sight down along the muzzle, tried to remember to aim low, but was afraid to point down lest he lose the ball again. The gun lurched up, down, right and left. It took all his strength to keep it still. His back hurt. The Hessians kept coming closer. Should he aim at someone, he wondered? Who?

He heard a click. The Frenchman had drawn back his flintlock. Jonathan pulled one of his hands away from his gun to do the same. The gun dipped dangerously. He grabbed the lock anyway, yanking back. It came with a snap.

"Steady!" shouted the Corporal. "Steady!" Jonathan was sure the Corporal was shouting at him alone.

He watched the blue coats, the crossed white sashes, the tall yellow caps. They were, he thought, no more than two hundred feet away. Why are they here? he asked himself. Why are they coming toward me? He felt his skin prickle. His stomach hurt.

The Hessian officer shouted more words that Jonathan could not understand. Without warning, the Hessians began to shift, some to the right and some to the left, until as if by magic they were no longer three in a row but ten men to the line: an advancing wall.

"Almost!" cried the Corporal.

Again the Hessian officer shouted. Upon his command, the soldiers lowered their guns. Without missing a step they snapped their bayonets onto their guns, presenting the glistening blades directly at the Americans.

Jonathan tried to swallow. He could not. His throat was too stiff, too dry. He was so thirsty.

A sudden explosion burst from the American line. Someone had fired.

The Corporal screamed a curse. His horse reared.

Someone else fired.

A wave of hysteria welled up inside Jonathan. His arms tensed. Without meaning to, he pulled the trigger. There was a flash and an explosion as the musket jerked against his body, spinning him halfway around.

More guns fired. Explosions burst about his ears, the percussion punching him like unseen fists.

"Out of my way!" someone screamed at him, roughly shoving him aside. Jonathan almost fell as another man pushed past him. More explosions, this time in front of him. Someone began to cry, "O Lord, O Lord."

Jonathan's ears rang. His eyes were smarting. The air was thick with smoke, and stank.

He knew that he had to reload and shoot again, but he stood where he was, confused. Why were things happening so quickly? It was unfair. The smoke got thicker. He could not see through it to understand what was happening. On all sides guns kept shooting. Sometimes they went off two at a time. Then came long, terrible empty pauses when nothing happened at all. Then orange flashes burst through the smoke again. Through it all, Jonathan heard the Corporal's voice raging above the din: "In line! In line! In order, idiots! In order!"

The smoke shifted, briefly lifting. The Hessians moved closer yet, their lines unbroken, their bayonets thrust forward, their drum pounding, their fife screaming.

2:50

Jonathan plunged his hand into his cartridge case, took out a cartridge, and bit through the twisted paper end. Hurriedly he went through the loading steps, trying to think only of what he had to do, concentrating so hard his head hurt.

When his gun was once more loaded, he lifted it. Drawing back the lock, he looked about, prepared to fire. But there he paused, bewildered, not sure which way to shoot. A roar of muskets came from one side, followed by another. The wind seemed to rise. Nearby came a loud, thick sound, a heavy "Huff!" as if someone had lost his breath. A weight fell against him, then tumbled to the ground. Jonathan stepped aside. His father's friend lay upon the ground, his legs twisted under him, eyes open wide, arms flung to either side, his sweaty blouse red with blood.

"In order! In order!" came the Corporal's piercing cry.

Jonathan knelt by the fallen man's side.

Another crash of gunfire came, followed by another.

Jonathan put his hand to the man's face, touching it with shaking fingers. The flesh was soft, wet, and warm.

Jonathan reached for his gun. It wasn't where he thought it was. Turning, he found it, but when he pulled at it, it wouldn't come. His eyes followed its line. The gun was caught under someone's twisting body—the Frenchman's.

Afraid to get closer, Jonathan's first thought was to leave the gun. Just as quickly, he told himself that he had to get it, that it wasn't his but borrowed, that he had to bring it back. It was his responsibility, his duty, his word.

Twisting awkwardly, the Frenchman lurched up on his hands and knees. His head, hanging low, moved from side to side. Blood dripped to the ground.

With a growing sense of horror, Jonathan took up the gun, then stood. The smoke had cleared from the road. The Hessian line was standing erect, guns high, aiming. As he watched, one of the Hessians dropped his gun and crumpled forward, his bright, golden cap hitting the ground and bouncing twice before it came to rest.

The Corporal had a musket in his hands and was reloading. His lips were drawn back from his teeth.

Jonathan searched for other Americans. They seemed to have gone. He whirled about. He saw them behind him, quickly backing away.

A shout came from the Hessian lines. Jonathan turned again. The Hessians had lowered their guns. Their bayonets were thrust forward ready to charge. As Jonathan watched, they began to trot forward, directly toward where he stood.

With a shock he realized that he was standing alone, and that the entire line of enemy troops was rushing at him and at no one else.

He spun about and began to run.

Jonathan ran away from the road, tripping, sprawling, falling on his knees. In one motion he sprang up, using his gun as a staff, and twisted to look back. A rapid rattle of musket shots came from a completely unexpected place. He stood transfixed, feeling lost, incapable of deciding which way to go. Where had the others gone? Where was the Corporal? Why hadn't they waited? Why hadn't they taken him along?

In his confusion, Jonathan turned a half circle, only to see three Hessian soldiers charging in his direction.

"*Halt!*" came the cry.

One of the soldiers stopped, lifted his gun, and fired. Jonathan saw the plume of flame, and heard the hard report. Whirling, he ran again.

He ran in terror, straining every muscle, pumping his legs, his arms, not daring to look back. His only salvation was the protection of the woods—he plunged among the trees. Several times the heavy gun almost slipped from his hands. He clutched at it frantically, grabbing it back when it started to fall as if it were the linchpin that held what was left of him together.

Shouts and shots pursued him from behind, branches and vines caught at him. His side ached terribly. His cartridge box and powder horn kept banging against his knees. Pulling them from around his neck, he flung them away. His foot caught upon a root. He crashed down, seeing

nothing but a blur of green, his breath blown, completely spent, leaving him without the strength to move at all.

3:05

He lay upon the ground telling himself that he had to get up. Yet he could not. Exhausted, he remained where he was. Gunshots crackled dimly in the distance. A whispering wind, carrying the echo of the fife, floated high. Then it all grew faint and fainter still until the only sounds were forest sounds. Soon they too drifted from his mind, leaving only silence.

In the immense silence all that Jonathan could hear was his own breath. It came at first in short, reaching gasps. As it slowed to normal, he felt a pain growing inside, a pain spreading through his body, pressing from within.

He began to cry. The cry came at first in pieces, as if the cry itself had been shattered and existed only in fragmentary, jagged bits. But bit by bit the cry grew whole, taking over until every part of him cried.

Deep, racking sobs came then, dry and hard. He felt a terrible loneliness. He did not know what he was or what would become of him. He did not know what to do, where to go. All he knew was pain.

MEET AVI (WORTIS), AUTHOR

Born into a family of writers, Avi confesses: "Not surprising I was a big reader, reading all sorts of things, children's books, adult books, and not the least, comic books. Beyond reading, my grandparents were excellent storytellers and my mother read to me and my twin sister nightly. I can even recall telling my own tales of adventure to a slightly younger cousin when quite young. I do believe that if you want to be a writer you have to read a lot."

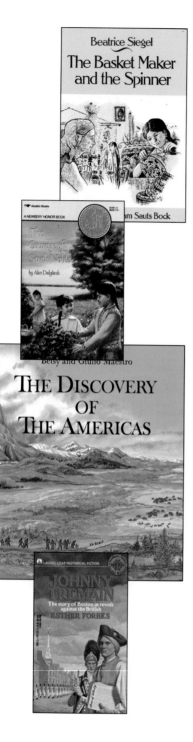

BIBLIOGRAPHY

The Basket Maker and the Spinner by Beatrice Siegel. The daily lives of a Native American basket weaver and a colonial spinner are compared in this book.

The Courage of Sarah Noble by Alice Dalgliesh. An eight-year-old girl's courage is tested as she is forced to stay with a Native American family in the Connecticut wilderness while her father leaves to get the rest of her family.

The Discovery of the Americas by Betsy and Giulio Maestro. Who came to America before the Pilgrims? Read about the exciting journeys of early explorers.

Johnny Tremain by Esther Forbes. A young Boston boy experiences dramatic historical events during the Revolutionary War as he gets involved with Paul Revere, Samuel Adams, and John Hancock.

The Legend of the White Doe by William H. Hooks. The disappearance of the settlers at Roanoke is explained in legend as Virginia Dare, the first English child born in the Americas, falls in love with a young Native American.

Sarah Morton's Day: A Day in the Life of a Pilgrim Girl by Kate Waters. In this book, photos show the typical day in the life of a nine-year-old girl in 1627.

War Comes to Willy Freeman by Christopher and James Lincoln Collier. Wilhelmina, a free thirteen-year-old African-American girl living in Connecticut, courageously faces the horrors of the Revolutionary War as she searches for her mother, who was taken prisoner by the British.

What's the Big Idea, Ben Franklin? by Jean Fritz. Discover the fascinating career of Benjamin Franklin, who started as a young Boston printer and became an internationally known inventor, writer, and politician.

GLOSSARY

PRONUNCIATION KEY

a as in at	o as in ox	ou as in out	ch as in chair
ā as in late	ō as in rose	u as in up	hw as in which
â as in care	ô as in bought	ûr as in turn;	ng as in ring
ä as in father	and raw	germ, learn,	sh as in shop
e as in set	oi as in coin	firm, work	th as in thin
ē as in me	o͝o as in book	ə as in about,	t͟h as in there
i as in it	o͞o as in too	chicken, pencil,	zh as in treasure
ī as in kite	or as in form	cannon, circus	

The mark (ˊ) is placed after a syllable with a heavy accent,
as in **chicken** (chikˊ ən).
The mark (ˊ) after a syllable shows a lighter accent,
as in **disappear** (disˊ ə pērˊ).

accustomed (ə kusˊ təmd) *adj.* Used to something.

acquire (ə kwīrˊ) *v.* To obtain; to get.

acre (āˊ kər) *n.* An amount of land that is about one-third of a city block in size; 43,560 square feet.

advisor (ad vīˊ zər) *n.* A person whose job is to consult and give opinions.

affable (afˊ ə bəl) *adj.* Pleasant and courteous.

agate (agˊ it) *n.* A playing marble with swirls or stripes of several colors in it.

agent (āˊ jənt) *n.* Someone who represents or stands in for another person.

agitated (ajˊ i tā dəd) *adj.* Excited.

ally (alˊ ī) *n.* A person who fights on the same side as another person.

alter (ôlˊ tər) *v.* To change; to make different.

archeologist (ärˊ kē olˊ ə jist) *n.* A scientist who learns about people from the past by digging up and studying things they left behind.

architect (ärˊ ki tektˊ) *n.* A person who designs buildings.

arctic (ärk´ tik) *adj.* Having to do with the region of the North Pole.

artifact (är´ tə fakt´) *n.* A handmade object from an earlier time or culture.

authority (ə thor´ i tē) *n.* A person who has the legal power or right to do something.

ballast (bal´ əst) *n.* Something added to increase weight and stability.

barbarian (bär bâr´ ē ən) *n.* A person who is not civilized; a brute; a savage.

bargaining (bär´ gə ning) *n.* Discussing terms; talking or arguing in order to agree upon something.

barge (bärj) *v.* To rudely push oneself into a place.

barrack (bar´ ək) *n.* Usually **barracks:** A large, simple building in which many people have beds.

battlement (bat´ l mənt) *n.* The high peaked towers of a wall used to protect a city.

bayonet (bā´ ə nit) *n.* A sharp weapon attached to the end of a rifle.

befall (bi fôl´) *v.* To happen to.

bequeath (bi kwēth´) *v.* To leave something to another person when one dies.

beset (bi set´) *v.* To surround.

bewilderment (bi wil´ dər mənt) *n.* Confusion.

blubber (blub´ ər) *n.* Whale fat.

bonito (bə nē´ tō) *n.* A fish similar to the mackerel, found in the Atlantic Ocean.

bound (bound) *v.* Past tense of **bind:** To tie up with a band or cord.

bow (bou) *n.* The curved front part of a boat.

brace (brās) *n.* A pair; a couple.

brazier (brā´ zhər) *n.* A metal frame for holding fire.

breed (brēd) *v.* To have young; to reproduce.

brutality (broo tal´ i tē) *n.* Cruelty; extremely harsh treatment.

bunker (bung´ kər) *n.* A room or building that is partly underground, used as a bomb shelter.

bureaucrat (byoor´ ə krat´) *n.* A government official; a person who works for the government.

Pronunciation Key: at; lāte; câre; fäther; set; mē; it; kīte; ox; rōse; ô in bought; coin; boŏk; toō; form; out; up; tûrn; ə sound in about, chicken, pencil, cannon, circus; chair; hw in which; ring; shop; thin; there; zh in treasure.

caisson (kā´ son) *n.* A tube-shaped structure used by workers when digging tunnels and underground rooms.

calculate (kal´ kyə lāt´) *v.* To measure; to figure out.

calumet (kal´ yə met´) *n.* A long, decorated pipe used in ceremonies by Native Americans.

canter (kan´ tər) *v.* To gallop slowly.

capsize (kap´ sīz) *v.* To overturn in the water, as a boat.

card (kärd) *n.* An instrument used for combing cotton or wool fibers.

caribou (kar´ ə boō´) *n.* A large deer, related to the reindeer.

cartridge (kär´ trij) *n.* A case containing explosives used as ammunition.

casement (kās´ mənt) *n.* A window that opens outward.

chaff (chaf) *n.* The husks of grain.

chafing (chā´ fing) *n.* A rubbing.

chattel (chat´ l) *n.* Anything movable that is owned by someone.

chisel (chiz´ əl) *n.* A cutting tool for wood or stone.

churn (chûrn) *v.* To make butter.

civility (si vil´ i tē) *n.* Courtesy.

civilization (siv´ ə lə zā´ shən) *n.* A culture, society, or group of human beings who have developed art, education, agriculture, trade, science, government, and so on.

clap (klap) *v.* To put forcefully and quickly.

coaxing (kōks´ ing) *n.* Urging; convincing.

cobbler (kob´ lər) *n.* A person who makes and repairs shoes and boots.

colliery (kol´ yə rē) *n.* A coal mine.

colonist (kol´ ə nist) *n.* A person who is a member of a settlement formed by people who have come to a new land.

colony (kol´ ə nē) *n.* A settlement formed by people who have come to a new land.

commemorate (kə mem´ ə rāt´) *v.* To honor by remembering.

commission (kə mish´ ən) *v.* To give someone authority to do something.

comprise (kəm prīz´) *v.* To contain; to include.

compromise (kom´ prə mīz´) *n.* A settlement made by both sides' giving up a little.

concentrated (kon´ sən trā´ tid) *adj.* Packed closely together.

confide (kən fīd´) *v.* To tell secrets to; to discuss private thoughts.

consent (kən sent´) *n.* Agreement.

constable (kon´ stə bəl) *n.* A police officer.

constellation (kon´ stə lā´ shən) *n.* A group of fixed stars having a name.

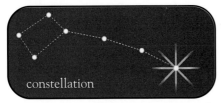

constellation

contemporary (kən tem´ pə rer´ ē) *n.* A person who lives in the same time period as others.

cord (kord) *n.* A measure, usually of wood, eight feet long by four feet wide and four feet high.

council (koun´ səl) *n.* An assembly that discusses and decides.

county seat (koun´ tē sēt´) *n.* The town in which the government of a county is housed.

courier (kûr´ ē ər) *n.* A messenger; a person who carries messages.

cranny (kran´ ē) *n.* A slit; a small opening in a rock wall.

crevasse (krə vas´) *n.* A deep crack in a glacier or in the earth's surface.

crimson (krim´ zən) *adj.* Deep red in color.

cubicle (kyoo´ bi kəl) *n.* A small enclosed space within a larger room.

cultivator (kul´ tə vā´ tər) *n.* A machine that loosens the soil before crops are planted.

cultivator

culturally (kul´ chər ə lē) *adv.* Having to do with the civilization of a given race or nation.

cylinder (sil´ in dər) *n.* Something shaped like a roller or a tube.

daze (dāz) *n.* Confusion; bewilderment.

debate (di bāt´) *v.* To argue; to discuss.

decidedly (di sī´ did lē) *adv.* Certainly.

defy (di fī´) *v.* To disobey openly or boldly.

descendant (di sen´ dənt) *n.* A child; an offspring; someone born in the family of a certain ancestor.

despair (di spâr´) *n.* Hopelessness.

determination (di tûr´ mə nā´ shən) *n.* Strong willpower; strength of will.

dignitary (dig´ ni ter´ ē) *n.* A person of high rank.

din (din) *n.* A lot of noise; clamor; uproar; racket.

dinghy (ding´ gē) *n.* A small boat.

dismantle (dis man´ tl) *v.* To take apart.

dispatch (di spach´) *n.* A message.

dissenter (di sen´ tər) *n.* One who differs or disagrees.

distinctly (di stingkt´ lē) *adv.* Clearly.

distinguish (di sting´ gwish) *v.* To notice a difference.

diverse (di vûrs´) *adj.* Different; varied.

domestic (də mes´ tik) *adj.* Belonging to or concerning the home.

dysentery (dis´ ən ter´ ē) *n.* A disease of the large intestines.

edict (ē´ dikt) *n.* A proclaimed law or order.

efficiency (i fish´ ən sē) *n.* Ability; skill; effectiveness.

efficient (i fish´ ənt) *adj.* Skillful; effective; capable.

empire (em´ pīr) *n.* A union of countries under the rule of a single ruler or government.

enforce (en fors´) *v.* 1. To urge with force. 2. To make people obey a law.

episode (ep´ ə sōd´) *n.* A story part or section with a plot that is separate from the main story.

ethnically (eth´ nik lē) *adv.* Having to do with the national origins of a people.

excavate (eks´ kə vāt´) *v.* To dig out.

expedition (ek´ spi dish´ ən) *n.* A journey made to accomplish something.

facade (fə säd´) *n.* The face or front of a building.

face (fās) *v.* To cover the outside of something with a different material.

faint (fānt) *adj.* Dim; weak; not clear.

falter (fôl´ tər) *v.* To be tongue-tied; to talk awkwardly.

famine (fam´ in) *n.* A scarcity of food; starvation.

fate (fāt) *n.* The power that is believed to cause events to happen as they do.

fatiguing (fə tē´ ging) *adj.* Tiring; exhausting.

feat (fēt) *n.* A notable deed; an exploit.

fell (fel) *v.* To cut down.

fiber (fī´ bər) *n.* Material or cloth.

fife (fīf) *n.* A small flute that makes a shrill sound.

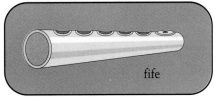

fife

flail (flāl) *n.* An instrument for threshing grain.

flint (flint) *n.* A hard stone that can produce sparks when struck against steel.

flung (flung) *v.* Past tense of **fling:** To hurl; to throw.

foal (fōl) *n.* A young horse.

fodder (fod´ ər) *n.* Cattle food.

foundry (foun´ drē) *n.* A place where metal is melted and formed.

fowling piece (fou´ ling pēs´) *n.* A shotgun used for shooting wild birds.

fragile (fraj´ əl) *adj.* Delicate; easily damaged.

fragrance (frā´ grəns) *n.* A sweet smell that is pleasing.

gabled (gā´ bəld) *adj.* Having gables, or small roofs that jut out from part of the main roof.

gaudy (gô´ dē) *adj.* Showy or flashy in a crude way.

girth (gûrth) *n.* The distance around something.

glacier (glā´ shər) *n.* A large, slow-moving mass of ice.

glassy (glas´ ē) *n.* A glass marble with colored swirls.

grave (grāv) *adj.* Serious.

grotesque (grō tesk´) *adj.* Fantastically, oddly, or unnaturally shaped.

gruel (grōō´ əl) *n.* A thin cereal boiled in water or milk.

grueling (grōō´ ə ling) *adj.* Very hard; tiring; exhausting.

Pronunciation Key: at; lāte; câre; fäther; set; mē; it; kīte; ox; rōse; ô in bought; coin; boŏk; tōō; form; out; up; tûrn; ə sound in about, chicken, pencil, cannon, circus; chair; hw in which; ring; shop; thin; *th*ere; zh in treasure.

handicap (han´ dē kap´) *n.* A disadvantage.

hardship (härd´ ship) *n.* Trouble; misfortune.

headland (hed´ lənd) *n.* A high piece of land that sticks out into a large body of water.

heap (hēp) *n.* A pile; a mound.

heritage (her´ i tij) *n.* Something handed down to a person from his or her ancestors.

hew (hyoō) *v.* To cut with an ax; to fell.

hibernate (hī´ bər nāt´) *v.* To pass the winter in a long sleep.

highwayman (hī´ wā´ mən) *n.* A robber on the highway; someone who robs travelers.

hogback (hôg´ bak´) *n.* A steep ridge.

hogback

horizon (hə rī´ zən) *n.* The distant line where the ocean and the sky seem to meet.

horsepower (hors´ pou´ ər) *n.* The measure of work a machine or an engine can do.

hostile (hos´ tl) *adj.* Unfriendly; threatening.

humiliated (hyoō mil´ ē ā tid) *adj.* Shamed; feeling one's pride hurt.

hysteria (hi ster´ ē ə) *n.* A condition of intense anxiety or excitement; a condition in which a person is extremely nervous.

ice cap (īs´ kap´) *n.* A thick layer of ice covering an area.

idler (īd´ lər) *n.* A person who is not working.

idly (īd´ lē) *adv.* Lazily.

immense (i mens´) *adj.* Very large or great; huge; enormous; vast.

impression (im presh´ ən) *n.* An idea; a picture in the mind.

impulse (im´ puls) *n.* Something done hastily or on the spur of the moment.

incident (in´ si dənt) *n.* An event; a happening.

inclined plane (in klīnd´ plān´) *n.* A slanted walkway; a ramp.

indentured servant (in den´ chərd sûr´ vənt) *n.* A person who came to America under a contract to work for someone else for a stated period of time.

indescribably (in´ di skrī´ bə blē) *adv.* Unusually; extraordinarily.

inefficient (in´ i fish´ ənt) *adj.* Unable to do something as well as it should be done.

inflammation (in´ flə mā´ shən) *n.* Pain, fever, and swelling in a part of the body.

inherit (in her´ it) *v.* To receive another's property after his or her death.

insert (in sûrt´) *v.* To put into.

insolent (in´ sə lənt) *adj.* Insulting; rude.

institution (in´ sti too´ shən) *n.* An organization that has a cause or a purpose.

insulation (in´ sə lā´ shən) *n.* A material that keeps heat from being lost.

intensity (in ten´ si tē) *n.* Concentration; fervor; passion.

intently (in tent´ lē) *adv.* Attentively; with great concentration.

interior (in tēr´ ē ər) *adj.* Inner; situated inside.

intolerable (in tol´ ər ə bəl) *adj.* Unbearable; impossible to endure.

invader (in vā´ dər) *n.* One who enters as an enemy.

investor (in ves´ tər) *n.* Someone who gives money to a company and expects to receive profits in return.

irons (ī´ ərnz) *n.* Chains to tie a person's wrists, ankles, or feet.

irritably (ir´ i tə blē) *adv.* In a way that shows annoyance.

johnny-cake (jon´ ē kāk´) *n.* A flat cornmeal bread or cake.

kidnap (kid´ nap) *v.* To seize and carry off a person.

kilometer (ki lom´ i tər) *n.* A measure of distance; about six-tenths of a mile.

laboriously (lə bor´ ē əs lē) *adv.* With difficulty.

laden (lād´ n) *adj.* Filled; loaded.

latke (lät´ kə) *n.* A potato pancake.

lavish (lav´ ish) *adj.* Extravagant; wasteful.

league (lēg) *n.* A distance of roughly three miles.

Pronunciation Key: at; lāte; câre; fäther; set; mē; it; kīte; ox; rōse; ô in bought; coin; bŏŏk; tōō; form; out; up; tûrn; ə sound in about, chicken, pencil, cannon, circus; chair; **hw** in which; ring; shop; thin; there; zh in treasure.

lever (lev′ ər) *n.* A sturdy, straight bar used for lifting up heavy weights.

linchpin (linch′ pin′) *n.* Something that holds parts together.

literacy (lit′ ər ə sē) *n.* The ability to read.

lodge (loj) *n.* A small house.

loft (lôft) *n.* A room directly below a roof; an attic.

loft

maim (mām) *v.* To injure seriously enough to disfigure or remove a body part.

malaria (mə lâr′ ē ə) *n.* A disease, usually accompanied by fever, caused by the bite of certain mosquitoes.

mallet (mal′ it) *n.* A wooden or rubber hammer.

manage (man′ ij) *v.* To be in charge of; to direct; to control.

maneuver (mə nōō′ vər) *v.* To change the position of something.

manor (man′ ər) *n.* The main house on an estate.

manual (man′ yōō əl) *adj.* Done by hand.

mare (mâr) *n.* A female horse.

mast (mast) *n.* A pole supporting a ship's sails.

meander (mē an′ dər) *v.* To wander aimlessly; to twist and turn at random.

measure (mezh′ ər) *n.* A container holding a specific amount.

mercenary (mûr′ sə ner′ ē) *n.* A hired soldier who fights for a foreign country for pay.

mill (mil) *n.* A factory; a place where grain is ground.

missionary (mish′ ə ner′ ē) *n.* Someone sent to another land to convert people to a religion.

mite (mīt) *adj.* A little bit.

momentous (mō men′ təs) *adj.* Very important.

monarch (mon′ ərk) *n.* A ruler; a king or queen.

monumental (mon′ yə men′ tl) *adj.* Large; imposing.

mortar (mor´ tər) *n.* A mixture of cement, lime, sand, and water, used in building brick or stone walls.

musket (mus´ kit) *n.* An old-fashioned kind of gun, used before the modern rifle.

mutilation (myo͞ot´ l ā´ shən) *n.* Injury; disfigurement by cutting, removing, or damaging a part.

nohow (nō´ hou´) *adv. nonstandard.* In no way.

nomadic (nō mad´ ik) *adj.* Wandering from place to place.

notion (nō´ shən) *n.* An idea.

obsolete (ob´ sə lēt´) *adj.* Not used anymore; out of date; old-fashioned.

obstacle (ob´ stə kəl) *n.* Something that gets in the way; a hindrance; an obstruction.

offense (ə fens´) *n.* An illegal act.

official (ə fish´ əl) *n.* A person who works for the government.

omen (ō´ mən) *n.* A sign of a future event.

opposition (op´ ə zish´ ən) *n.* Resistance; the act of being against something.

ornery (or´ nə rē) *adj.* Disagreeable.

outrageous (out rā´ jəs) *adj.* Not reasonable; offensive; insulting.

overawed (ō´ vər ôd´) *adj.* Extremely respectful or fearful.

overjoyed (ō´ vər joid´) *adj.* Extremely happy.

pagoda (pə gō´ də) *n.* A temple of the Far East, usually a tower with an upward curving roof at each story.

pagoda

parlor (pär´ lər) *n.* A sitting room set aside for seeing guests.

passage (pas´ ij) *n.* A narrow corridor; a hallway.

peat bog (pēt´ bog) *n.* A swampy area filled with partly decayed plant life.

peculiar (pi kyo͞ol´ yər) *adj.* Strange; unusual.

pemmican (pem´ i kən) *n.* A mixture of powdered dried meat, dried berries, and fat.

peninsula (pə nin´ sə lə) *n.* A piece of land that is surrounded on three sides by water.

Pronunciation Key: at; lāte; câre; fäther; set; mē; it; kīte; ox; rōse; ô in bought; coin; boŏk; toō; form; out; up; tûrn; ə sound in about, chicken, pencil, cannon, circus; chair; hw in which; ring; shop; thin; there; zh in treasure.

---

percussion (pər kush´ ən) *n.* A sharp blow to set off an artillery shell or other explosive.

persecution (pûr´ si kyoō´ shən) *n.* Oppression; bad treatment.

persuade (pər swād´) *v.* To lead another person to agree with oneself; to sway.

peruse (pə roōz´) *v.* To read over; to study.

pester (pes´ tər) *v.* To harrass; to annoy; to bother.

petition (pə tish´ ən) *v.* To make a written request.

pharaoh (fâr´ ō) *n.* The title of the kings of ancient Egypt.

phenomenally (fi nom´ ə nə lē) *adv.* Remarkably; by a miracle.

pilgrim (pil´ grim) *n.* 1. A person who travels to a holy place. 2. **Pilgrim:** A member of a religious group that came to America to find freedom of religion.

piñon (pin´ yən) *n.* A kind of pine tree with edible seeds.

pitch (pich) *n.* A dark, sticky substance used to make things waterproof.

porcelain (por´ sə lin) *n.* A fine, delicate china.

portion (por´ shən) *v.* To share among; to distribute.

practice (prak´ tis) *n.* The usual way of doing something.

prevailing (pri vā´ ling) *adj.* The most frequent; occurring most often.

profitable (prof´ i tə bəl) *adj.* Making gains; making money.

prominent (prom´ ə nənt) *adj.* Important; well-known.

pronto (pron´ tō) *adv.* Quickly.

prophecy (prof´ ə sē) *n.* A prediction of the future; a foretelling.

province (prov´ ins) *n.* A division of a country; a specific region.

provisions (prə vizh´ ənz) *n.* Things that are supplied for a special task, especially food and the necessary tools.

pursue (pər soō´) *v.* To chase.

quarry (kwor´ ē) *v.* To dig out of a pit. —*n.* A pit from which stone is dug.

quarter (kwor´ tər) *n.* Usually
quarters: Living
accommodations; a place to live.

quiver (kwiv´ ər) *v.* To tremble; to
shake with a quick, slight motion.

radical (rad´ i kəl) *adj.* Having
strong, often extreme, convictions
or opinions and demanding
changes without compromise.

rambunctious (ram bungk´ shəs)
adj. Active and noisy in a violent
way.

rampart (ram´ pärt) *n.* A wall used
as a defense for a city.

range (rānj) *n.* A large, unfenced
area of land on which cattle and
sheep graze.

rankle (rang´ kəl) *v.* To cause
bitterness.

ration (rash´ ən) *n.* A fixed
allowance of something; a limited
share.

realm (relm) *n.* A kingdom; all the
area controlled by one ruler.

reap (rēp) *v.* To cut grain.

recruit (ri krōōt´) *v.* To gain fresh
people for a task.

reedy (rē´ dē) *adj.* Like a sound
made by a reed instrument such as
the clarinet.

relate (ri lāt´) *v.* To tell.

relations (ri lā´ shənz) *n.* The
connections between people;
people's associations with each
other; the dealings people have
with each other.

relentless (ri lent´ lis) *adj.* Pitiless;
harsh.

reliable (ri lī ´ ə bəl) *adj.*
Dependable; trustworthy.

relief (ri lēf´) *n.* A piece of art in
which the figures stand out from a
flat background.

remains (ri mānz´) *n.* Something
that is left after a period of time.

rendezvous (rän´ də vōō´) *n.* A
meeting.

renew (ri nōō´) *v.* To repair; to
restore.

restless (rest´ lis) *adj.* Unable to
rest or stay in one place.

restrain (ri strān´) *v.* To hold back;
to control.

ridicule (rid´ i kyōōl´) *v.* To make
fun of; to mock.

rigid (rij´ id) *adj.* Fixed; set in one
position or expression.

Pronunciation Key: at; lāte; câre; fäther; set; mē; it; kīte; ox; rōse; ô in bought; coin; bŏŏk; tōō; form; out; up; tûrn; ə sound in about, chicken, pencil, cannon, circus; chair; hw in which; ring; shop; thin; there; zh in treasure.

runnel (run´l) *n.* A small stream or channel. *Used as a verb in the story:* To make streams or channels.

rush (rush) *n.* A long-stemmed water plant.

sandspit (sand´spit) *n.* A bar of raised sand that juts out from an island.

sap (sap) *v.* To weaken; to destroy in a sneaky way.

sarcophagus (sär kof´ə gəs) *n.* A coffin made of stone.

satchel (sach´əl) *n.* A small bag; a school bag.

scarce (skârs) *adj.* Hard to obtain; rare.

scavenge (skav´inj) *v.* To gather discarded material; to look for things that people have thrown away.

scoff (skôf) *v.* To mock; to jeer; to laugh at in a sneering way.

scullery (skul´ə rē) *n.* A small room off the kitchen where dishes are washed, vegetables are prepared, and other chores are done.

scurvy (skûr´vē) *n.* A disease caused by a lack of vitamin C, a vitamin found in fresh fruits and vegetables.

seep (sēp) *v.* To flow a little at a time.

serpent (sûr´pənt) *n.* A snake.

settlement (set´l mənt) *n.* A colony; a new community in a new land.

sheaves (shēvz) *n.* Plural of **sheaf:** A bundle of grain.

shirk (shûrk) *v.* To avoid work or duty.

shrewd (shrōōd) *adj.* Keen; observant; sharp.

sickle (sik´əl) *n.* An instrument with a curved blade for cutting grain.

silo (sī´lō) *n.* A tall building for storing food for animals on a farm.

sinew (sin´yōō) *n.* A tough substance that joins muscle to bone; a tendon.

sixpence (siks´pəns) *n. British.* The sum of six pennies.

skirt (skûrt) *v.* To move around the edge of.

sledge (slej) *n.* A sled or sleigh.

sleeper (slē′ pər) *n. chiefly British.*
A railroad tie.

sole (sōl) *adj.* Single; one and only.

solely (sōl′ lē) *adv.* Only.

species (spē′ shēz) *n.* A plant or
animal family; a kind of plant or
animal.

spectator (spek′ tā tər) *n.* One
who looks on or watches.

speculator (spek′ yə lā′ tər) *n.* A
person who buys things hoping to
sell them later at a higher price.

spent (spent) *adj.* Exhausted; used
up.

spout (spout) *v.* To come out
through a narrow opening with
great force. —*n.* The end of a
tube or pipe that sticks out of
something so that the contents
can pour out.

spout

S.S. Schutzstaffel (shoōts′ stä′ fəl)
German. A special Nazi police
force.

stag (stag) *n.* An adult male deer.

stallion (stal′ yən) *n.* An adult
male horse.

stank (stangk) *v.* A past tense of
stink: To give off an unpleasant
smell.

startling (stärt′ ling) *adj.*
Surprising; astonishing.

stationary (stā′ shə ner′ ē) *adj.*
Still; unmoving.

stave (stāv) *n.* One of the thin,
curved wood strips used to make a
barrel.

steadily (sted′ ə lē) *adv.* In a
regular or methodical way.

steed (stēd) *n.* A high-spirited
horse.

stifled (stī′ fəld) *adj.* Suffocated or
smothered.

stock (stok) *n.* The part of a gun to
which the barrel is attached.

stunt (stunt) *n.* A display of daring;
a clever, showy trick. —*v.* To stop
the growth of.

suffocate (suf′ ə kāt′) *v.* To
smother; to choke; to die from
lack of air.

survey (sər vā′) *v.* To measure the
land.

surveyor (sər vā′ ər) *n.* A person
whose job is to measure tracts of
land exactly.

Pronunciation Key: at; lāte; câre;
fäther; set; mē; it; kīte; ox; rōse; ô in
bought; coin; boŏk; tōō; form; out; up;
tûrn; ə sound in about, chicken, pencil,
cannon, circus; chair; hw in which;
ring; shop; thin; there; zh in treasure.

---

tarmac (tär´ mak) *n.* A road
covering made of tar, crushed
stone, and bitumen, or asphalt.

taunt (tônt) *v.* To sneer at; to
ridicule.

terrain (tə rān´) *n.* The type of
natural features in an area of land.

textile (teks´ tīl) *n.* A woven
fabric.

thatch (thach) *v.* To cover a roof
with straw or similar material.

thrash (thrash) *v.* To thresh; to
beat the grain from stalks.

thresh (thresh) *v.* To separate
grain from the stalk by beating it.

thresher (thresh´ ər) *n.* A machine
that separates grain from the stalk.

tidal (tīd´ l) *adj.* Having to do with
the rise and fall of the sea.

tide (tīd) *n.* A current or flowing
water.

token (tō´ kən) *n.* A sign; a
symbol.

toll-gate (tōl´ gāt´) *n.* A gate where
people must pay in order to use a
road.

tomb (tōōm) *n.* A monument in
which a dead person is buried.

torment (tor ment´) *v.* To inflict
pain; to torture.

tousle (tou´ zəl) *v.* To make
disordered or messy.

trace (trās) *n.* One of the two
straps or chains that connect an
animal to a load being pulled.

tradition (trə dish´ ən) *n.* A
custom that has been handed
down or preserved through many
generations.

transfixed (trans fikst´) *adj.* Held
completely still due to terror;
frozen by fear.

transform (trans form´) *v.* To make
different; to change completely.

translation (trans lā´ shən) *n.*
Something written or spoken that
is changed from one language to
another.

trek (trek) *n.* A difficult journey or
trip.

trench (trench) *n.* A ditch; a long,
narrow channel.

tribute (trib´ yōōt) *n.* Praise given
in recognition of worth or value.

trifling (trī´ fling) *adj.* Not
important.

triumphantly (trī um´ fənt lē) *adv.*
Successfully; victoriously.

trot (trot) *n.* A slow run. —*v.* To run slowly.

typhus (tī′ fəs) *n.* An infectious disease spread by lice and fleas.

unclench (un klench′) *v.* To open; to relax.

unconscious (un kon′ shəs) *adj.* Without physical or mental awareness; senseless.

unison (yōō′ nə sən) *n. idiom:* **in unison:** In perfect agreement; moving exactly together.

unwieldy (un wēl′ dē) *adj.* Bulky; awkward; unmanageable.

upheaval (up hē′ vəl) *n.* A violent change or disturbance.

urge (ûrj) *v.* To beg; to persuade.

urgent (ûr′ jənt) *adj.* Needing immediate attention.

utterly (ut′ ər lē) *adv.* Completely; absolutely; totally.

venture (ven′ chər) *n.* A new business that involves risk.

veranda (və ran′ də) *n.* A covered balcony; a porch.

via (vī′ ə) *adv.* By way of; passing through.

viaduct (vī′ ə dukt′) *n.* A set of railroad tracks or a road that is raised above ground level.

vigorous (vig′ ər əs) *adj.* Physically strong.

vital (vīt′ l) *adj.* Very important.

wash (wosh) *n.* An area of land that has been shaped partly by the action of water moving over it.

water buffalo (wô′ tər buf′ ə lō) *n.* A kind of oxen with large curved horns and bluish-black hide. Water buffaloes are trained to work in rice fields in Asia.

W.C. Water closet: A bathroom.

wedge (wej) *n.* A **V**-shaped piece of wood or metal used for splitting, forcing open, holding, or fastening.

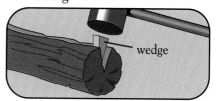
wedge

wick (wik) *n.* A braided or twisted string of a soft substance that soaks up the fuel in a candle or lamp and holds the flame.

wreckage (rek′ ij) *n.* The remains of something that has been wrecked or destroyed.

zephyr (zef′ ər) *n.* The west wind.

continued from page 5

COLOPHON

This book has been designed in the classic style to emphasize our commitment to classic literature. The typeface, Goudy Old Style, was drawn in 1915 by Frederic W. Goudy, who based it on fifteenth-century Italian letterforms.

The art has been drawn to reflect the golden age of children's book illustration and its recent rebirth in the work of innovative artists of today. This book was designed by John Grandits. Composition, electronic page makeup, and photo and art management were provided by The Chestnut House Group, Inc.